MAD DOGS AND AN ENGLISH GIRL

CAROLINE WATERMAN

MAD DOGS AND AN ENGLISH GIRL

Matador
9 De Montfort Mews
Leicester LE1 7FW, UK
Tel: (+44) 116 255 9311 / 9312
Email: books@troubador.co.uk
Web: www.troubador.co.uk/matador

ISBN 978-1905886-937

Typeset in 11.5pt Bembo by Troubador Publishing Ltd, Leicester, UK
Printed in the UK by The Cromwell Press Ltd, Trowbridge, Wilts, UK

To all my wonderful friends in Spain, my family,
and also my friend, Kate, for all her help and encouragement

Ancha es Castilla y que hermosa
La tristeza enorme de sus soledades,
La tristeza llena de sol, de aire, de cielo.

(Wide is Castile and how beautiful
The tremendous sadness of its lonely places,
 A sadness filled with sun, air and sky.)

Miguel de Unamuno
Poet and philosopher who was critical of
Franco and died during the Spanish Civil War

CHAPTER ONE

ARRIVAL

The sweltering heat inside the railway carriage added immeasurably to my discomfort. Excitement, apprehension and the rigours of third class rail travel had all combined to make sure I had not slept a wink during the long night journey from Paris; and now, on top of all that, this suffocating, merciless heat! I was beginning to wonder how much longer I could survive.

The air was filled with a cocktail of sweat, cigarette smoke, half-digested garlic and the stench of caged chickens. These unhappy creatures, crammed into the luggage rack above my head, pecked at the wire from time to time in protest at their imprisonment. Opposite me, a large woman occupying at least two seats, was attempting ineffectively to cool herself with an improvised fan made from a newspaper. She kept wiping her brow with her forearm muttering: *"madre mía! madre mía!"* to which the other suffering passengers would respond with sympathetic nods and grunts of agreement. At least it was reassuring to note that these temperatures were excessive even for Spaniards.

I felt beads of perspiration trickling down my forehead into my eyes as I sat firmly wedged between the side of the carriage and a group of burly Basque workmen. They had boarded the train at a small, rather ugly village with a long, unpronounceable name way back in the foothills of the Pyrenees. Their faces were round and red under black berets and their shirts clung stickily to their muscular bodies. They spoke to each other in an unintelligible language but I noticed they switched back to Spanish the minute a civil guard appeared – which was frequently as there were several of them roaming about the train.

After a while I felt compelled to ask the Basques about this strange language of theirs. The one sitting next to me looked quickly around before replying in a low voice.

"Yes, this is our own language. Of course we speak it among ourselves, but now we have to be very careful, you know, because it's forbidden."

"Forbidden? But why?"

He shrugged his shoulders. "That's the way it is here. They don't like it. A friend of ours was caught speaking it and they took him away. We found him next day unconscious in a back street: hardly recognisable. That's how things are now."

This last chilling remark brought home to me that I was about to experience life in a Police State. I wondered what I would make of it.

As soon as the other passengers discovered that I spoke reasonable Spanish they bombarded me with questions. I explained to them that I was English, nineteen years old and on my way to Burgos where I would spend a year with a family teaching English and hopefully, improving my Spanish at the same time. The fat lady opposite leaned forward and tapped me on the knee.

"You are brave, señorita, to travel like this on your own. A young girl like you shouldn't really be travelling alone, you know." (How many more times was I to hear that!)

"Have you come all the way across France?" she continued. "You must be tired."

"Yes, I am a bit," I confessed, remembering those hard leather seats and the seemingly endless night; but here the wooden third class seats were even harder and the train much slower. I glanced down at my watch. Surely we must be arriving soon? I had already learned from a previous visit that the railways, like everything else in Spain, were blissfully unaware of the existence of Time. Nobody ever seemed in a hurry and it just wasn't important. Ours being a mail train, we had stopped at every village and occasionally the driver stepped down onto the platform to stretch his legs and have a chat with the station master – so the realisation that we should have arrived at Burgos an hour ago came as no surprise.

I decided that I too had to stretch my cramped limbs so I

squeezed out of my seat and struggled towards the corridor which was packed with soldiers smoking, laughing and shouting to one another. They eyed me with curiosity as I pushed past them. Reaching an open window, I thrust my head out into the flow of warm air which rushed against my face, covering it with smuts. Gazing at the bleak landscape, glimpsed through clouds of steam, I wondered about Burgos. I knew nothing about the place except what a friend of mine, Julio, had told me: that it was an ancient Castilian city with a famous cathedral, lying in the heart of the *meseta*.

I was reminded of this when I noticed that the countryside had changed considerably and not for the better. Gone were the wooded hills and rushing streams of the Basque Country. Instead I beheld a strange, monotonous panorama of yellow-grey stubble dotted with endless sheaves of wheat shimmering in the afternoon heat. The dust blew all about as the train passed and where there might once have been grass, it was now shrivelled and dead, exposing the rock-hard ground beneath. Workers could be seen toiling in the fields among their wilting crops. So this was the *meseta*, the Castilian plateau, a vast expanse of brown tree-less earth burning under a relentless sun. I had left my temperate homeland to come and live in this sad, impoverished wilderness. Madness! I thought: what was I doing?

From time to time, small villages appeared. Made of the earth and stones around them, they looked a natural part of the landscape, their small ochre hovels crouching under terracotta roofs usually clustered around a church belfry. Some appeared to have no roads linking them to the outside world – just earth tracks leading to the surrounding fields.

Then, suddenly, I noticed in the far distance, stretching skywards, two graceful spires silhouetted against the dark blue. Could this be Burgos cathedral? Excited, I hurried back to my compartment to consult my fellow travellers. They peered out of the window, and confirmed that yes, we were indeed approaching my destination.

As we neared the station, I started to assemble my few belongings, easing my case carefully down from between the crates of chickens. They resented the disturbance and clucked at me indignantly, poking their heads through the wire and pecking at my hands. The Basques laughed and came to my assistance.

I felt sorry to leave my fellow travellers as their cheerful company had done much to enliven this interminable journey. Listening to their life histories, it was even possible to forget, occasionally, the heat and smells. They had shown me photographs of their girlfriends and mothers, wives and children, shared their pig-skin bottle of wine and even entertained me with Basque songs when they were certain that there were no civil guards around. As we pulled into the station they wished me well and invited me to stay with them in their native village.

At last the elderly engine, to the accompaniment of creaks groans and hisses, ground ponderously to a halt and I clambered down onto the platform where the Basques handed me my case and bags from the carriage window.

"*Adiós!*" they said, each in turn shaking my hand. "And be careful! There are a lot of *them* in Burgos!"

With this parting warning they laughed heartily and waved me goodbye as the station master rang his bell. After a few seconds of last minute door slamming, the train, with a violent jerk, started off once more to continue its long, tedious journey to Madrid.

Now I was alone, quite alone, standing beside my small pile of luggage, enveloped in the blinding smoke of the engine's parting gift. I blinked and looked around wondering if anyone was there to meet me. I felt decidedly nervous as I knew little about my new employers.

Julio had found me the job. He was a Spaniard I had met in London where he was studying: an eccentric character, full of himself, but in such an amusing way that I couldn't help liking him. He fancied himself as an entrepreneur and was constantly throwing time and money at unsuccessful projects, convinced that one day he would become seriously rich. My own aspirations were more modest. I worked in tourism and believed that becoming fluent in Spanish could improve my chances of promotion so I asked Julio to find me a job in Spain. This he succeeded in doing on one of his visits home. He had recommended me to a doctor he knew slightly in Burgos who was looking for a girl to live in and teach English to his family. Julio returned to England with the good news and straight away I left my job in London and set off for Spain.

Hearing a shout, I looked round and saw, as the steam gradually cleared, two figures approaching me. They resolved themselves into a middle-aged man and a young girl. The man, whom I took to be the doctor, was short, plump and swarthy. He had heavy features and small, black eyes that pinned themselves on me disconcertingly. I held out my hand.

"Doctor Vázquez?" I enquired. He took a step nearer.

"Yes." He looked me up and down in the way I had seen farmers cast their experienced eyes over cattle in a market. "How are you? Your train is late."

His podgy hand met mine and instinctively I wanted to recoil from him. I had been told that first impressions were usually reliable so this was less than reassuring.

"Yes, I know," I said wearily, gathering up my things, "I'm sorry you've had to wait so long."

The girl, who had been standing behind Vázquez, now stepped forward and to my surprise, kissed me affectionately on both cheeks.

"Don't worry," she said. "It doesn't matter. The trains are always late. The main thing is that you've arrived safely. Welcome to Burgos!"

"This is my assistant and secretary," said Vázquez.

"Anita," said the girl, "my name's Anita."

I looked at her. She was about my age and very attractive with short, black curls and lustrous, brown eyes. She was bronzed, her cheeks were rosy and she greeted me with a dazzling smile, displaying a row of pearly-white teeth. Her well-manicured nails were painted a delicate shade of pink to match her candy-striped dress. White stiletto-heeled sandals and gold earrings completed the picture and she smelt deliciously of some exotic perfume. What a sorry contrast I must make, I thought, hot and bedraggled, lank hair plastering my head, face bereft of make-up and covered in smuts, and a travel-stained dress clinging unflatteringly to my legs! But the warm and friendly manner of this girl won me over at once despite her irritatingly beautiful appearance and I had the feeling we were going to be friends.

We walked out of the station into the dazzling sunshine. Vázquez's car stood in the forecourt beside two shabby buses. One was a dirty yellow and the other of a colour that could no longer be distinguished. They were amazingly ancient and dilapidated, like exhibits for a transport museum prior to restoration. Several passengers, who had just got off the train, were climbing into the yellow one, this being in slightly better condition than the other whose driver was dozing in his seat. He looked up at us sleepily as we passed and then nodded off again. I later learned that these vehicles belonged respectively, to the two main hotels in Burgos, the Hotel España and the Hotel Ávila and between them they seemed to operate a kind of taxi service to and from the railway station.

From the car, bumping its way over the cobbled streets, I gained my first impressions of the place that was to become my new home. There was little traffic at that time of day, just an occasional cart drawn by mules or donkeys. I was surprised to see there were so few cars. The streets were narrow with crumbling buildings on either side rising higgledy-piggledy, clustered closely together. Behind their roofs rose the grey cathedral spires, elaborate and imposing, dominating their surroundings. Everywhere windows were shuttered against the August sun and few people were about at this siesta time.

A river ran through the town which we crossed by a wide bridge, entering a square empty save for a solitary policeman standing in the centre under a striped sunshade, looking hot and bored. He jumped to attention as we approached and waved us on with exaggerated gestures despite there being no other traffic. From the square we turned into a broad street where the car drew up beside a rather formidable doorway. We climbed out and Anita gave me another hug saying that she had to go but would see me again soon and introduce me to her friends. She tripped away and I was left alone with Vázquez.

"Come," he said and I followed him through the doorway and up several flights of wide stairs. It seemed very dark, coming in from the street, but deliciously cool.

"My wife is away at the moment," said Vázquez, "with the younger children and the nursemaid. They are in Santander holidaying but we shall be joining them there shortly. At present there is no one in the house but my eldest son, Tomasín, and me – and the maid, of course."

The flat was large, gloomy and old-fashioned, with ornate furniture and heavy velvet curtains. First, he showed me the living room which was full of ostentatious knick-knacks and gilt clocks ticking away noisily. In one corner stood a large pianola surrounded by spindly, flower-less plants. The rest of the room I could barely distinguish as the blinds were down and my eyes had not had time to adjust after the dazzling brightness outside.

Next, I followed him down a corridor to a vast dining room containing a long oak table. At the far end of the room was a conservatory filled with more plants and a silent canary perched despondently in a cage suspended from the ceiling.

I saw a boy standing on the other side of the room. He looked about fourteen, tall and spindly like the plants, and obviously going through an awkward, gawky stage of adolescence. He looked precocious for his age and I guessed that, as the eldest son, he was probably used to having his own way.

While his father and I talked, he stood nearby, lolling against the wall, chewing and staring at me, an insolent smile hovering about his lips.

"You will give the boy lessons in the morning and in the afternoon," said my new boss. "He knows some English. We had a girl before."

At that moment the maid entered the room to announce that lunch was ready. She was a small, shy girl with a quiet voice and downcast eyes. I noticed that she never looked at her employer and I had the impression that she was rather frightened of him.

I was longing to have a shower and change my clothes but Vázquez insisted there was no time as the meal was waiting. The three of us sat down at one end of the long table and the maid, whose name was Rosa, bustled backwards and forwards bringing the food and serving us. There was soup strongly flavoured with garlic, then fish, followed by meat and fruit all washed down with a strong, red wine.

I tucked in trying to ignore the fact that both Vázquez and his son kept staring at me while we ate, but I was hungry after my long journey and nothing was going to spoil my meal.

When we had finished, I was allowed to retire and Rosa showed me to my room. She explained that there were two bathrooms, one for the *servicio* (the servants), and another for the *señores*. I would be allowed to use that of the *señores* which was through the corridor at the other end of the flat.

"Have a good rest, señorita. I will bring you coffee later." So saying she closed the door quietly behind her and I was on my own.

I looked around the room but could see little as it was so dark. Walking over to the window I half opened the Venetian blinds and the light flooded in casting a pattern of stripes onto the bedspread. I saw that my room was sparsely furnished with a chest of drawers, a small cupboard and a wooden chair. Above the bed an image of the Virgin Mary gazed down at me with doleful, unseeing eyes. Not a happy Madonna this, but a sorrowful one, her arms spread out in a gesture of despair, tears rolling down her cheeks.

I opened my case and extracted a towel and some clean clothes. I couldn't be bothered to look for the *señores* bathroom and decided instead to use the servants' one which happened conveniently to be opposite my bedroom. I dived under a cool shower – something I had dreamt of during the hot journey – and revelled in its refreshing cascade of water. What bliss: to be cool *and* clean!

Back in my room I started to unpack and it was only then that I realised just how exhausted I was. I left the unpacking, kicked off my shoes and sank onto the bed where I lay, damp hair straddled across the pillow, staring up at the little reflections of light playing on the ceiling. Then I closed my eyes, listening to someone singing outside in the street. The next moment I was asleep.

ༀ ༃

I was woken three hours later by a gentle tapping on the door. Rosa entered with the promised cup of coffee and handed it to me shyly.

"The Doctor has left for the clinic," she said, "and I thought, ...that is..." She hesitated. "Yes?" I said encouragingly.

"I have a little time before cooking supper and I wondered if I could show you some of the city: go for a walk..."

"I'd love that! I'm dying to see Burgos!"

She smiled nervously. "I mustn't be long. Just a short walk."

Together we slipped out into the evening sunshine. It was much cooler now and the town was full of people. Indeed, it seemed that the entire population of Burgos had emerged for an evening stroll.

"I will show you the Espolón," said Rosa. "That is where everyone walks in the evening."

Having been in Spain before, I knew all about the ritual of the *paseo*, the obligatory evening walk which all self-respecting Spaniards took before their evening meal. It was one of the pleasanter aspects of Spanish life, an opportunity to wear your best clothes and look elegant for a couple of hours and an excuse to meet friends and have the odd drink with them. In most towns there was a favourite place for the *paseo*. Here, in Burgos, it was obviously the Espolón, a shady, river-side walk, free of traffic and well provided with bars and cafés, their tables and chairs scattered across the paving.

That evening it was so crowded that we had difficulty moving among the jostling, good-humoured throng. I invited Rosa to a drink and we sat down at one of the tables. There, under the trees sipping ice-cold beer, I was able to observe at leisure my new surroundings and their inhabitants. It was an extraordinary scene that seemed to belong to some bygone age – like being transported back in time, perhaps to a period resembling the British Edwardian era. There were uniformed nursemaids pushing prams accompanied by small girls in stiff, frilly dresses tied with silk sashes, and little boys, their hair newly-brushed and shoes polished, looking uncomfortably clean and tidy in immaculate white shirts. In stark contrast, I had noticed earlier that down on the river bank, barefoot, grubby children dressed in rags were wading in the muddy water.

Many of the nursemaids were enjoying the attentions of

soldiers and I was told later that this was a tradition. Certainly, the nursemaids had plenty of choice because Burgos was a military headquarters and there were soldiers everywhere. They were dishevelled and unkempt as they slouched along looking uncomfortable in uniforms which all seemed several sizes too big for them. Their faces were unshaven and their boots dusty but this did not seem to deter the giggling nursemaids who responded flirtatiously to their advances.

The other young men and women were all wearing their best clothes, the girls tripping along in high heels, arms linked, pretending unconvincingly that they were unaware of the muttered compliments thrown at them by passing youths. As they floated by, the heady scent of their mingled perfumes wafted towards us. There were married couples strolling along arm in arm, greeting their friends, exchanging jokes, and grannies dressed in black, taking their grandchildren for a walk. Groups of men sat in the cafes smoking, laughing, drinking wine and playing cards.

The atmosphere was so lively and intoxicating that I felt I could have stayed there all evening but alas, Rosa had to get back to start her cooking. She remained very quiet and shy and conversation with her was difficult. Only once did I manage to shake her defences when I asked her whether she had a boyfriend. She seemed taken aback by this innocent question and her pale face blanched even more. She shook her head and turned away in embarrassment, so I dropped the subject.

On the way back and after a long silence, she said as we approached the house: "I hope you will be happy here."

I replied that from what I had seen of Burgos so far, I thought I would be very happy.

"No, no, I mean here – in this house."

"Is there any reason why I shouldn't be?" Suddenly I felt uneasy. "Oh, and by the way, wasn't there another English girl staying here before me?"

Rosa gave me a strange look. "Yes, there was," she murmured in a voice so quiet I could barely distinguish her words, "but she didn't stay very long."

CHAPTER TWO

SANTANDER

It was not easy to teach English to Tomasín. In fact, it would not be an exaggeration to say that it was bordering on the impossible. Firstly, he had no interest whatsoever in learning the language and secondly, it was obvious that his youthful mind was busily occupied with matters altogether unrelated to his studies.

Breakfast was set for me each morning in the conservatory among the potted plants. Beside my cup of coffee lay a pile of English text books and sitting at the small, round table, waiting for me was my pupil, his long brown legs sprawled out in front of him. He greeted me, as I sat down beside him, with his usual insolent grin, his arms folded in a gesture of defiance. I took a sip of my coffee, thumbed through one of the books and then began optimistically.

"Today we are going to revise the irregular verbs. Turn to page twelve – we'll begin with the verbs 'to be' and 'to have', present tense..."

"I know them," interrupted the boy. "I like your hair. Is it natural? Most of the blondes in Spain use bleach."

"Please concentrate Tomasín! I want to hear the present tense of 'to be'. Have you found the right page?"

"You can tell they bleach it because you can see all the black bits coming through at the roots..."

"Concentrate! If you know the present tense we'll go on to the past. We'll look at it first and then you can say it to me from memory."

But he was not listening. He was not even looking at the book. Instead his eyes were firmly fixed on the neckline of my dress.

"Do you have a *novio* – a boyfriend?" he enquired plucking thoughtfully at the small black hairs sprouting on his upper lip.

"We are not here to discuss my private life. You are supposed to be learning English. Now, about these verbs –"

"I don't suppose English boys are much good – so cold!" he chuckled, amused at his own observations. "I've heard the men are all as cold as ice over there. Not like us!" His chuckles exploded into guffaws.

I sighed, trying to keep my patience. When his laughter had subsided I took a deep breath and tried again.

"I am waiting to hear the past tenses of 'to be', 'to have' and 'to go'. Please begin!"

"You've got a good figure too," he persisted, popping a piece of bubble gum into his mouth. "Better than the last girl we had. She was too fat round the middle and didn't have enough – you know — here!" With his hands he described invisible bosoms in the air in front of him and collapsed again in convulsions of mirth nearly causing him to choke on his bubble gum.

"Look Tomasín, – your father pays me to teach you English and that is what you are going to learn. Do you hear?"

"English is so boring. I think you could teach me other things!"

By this time my patience was beginning to wear thin and I was becoming exasperated. If no progress could be made with the boy's English, Vázquez would think I had been shirking and I might lose my job. While I was wrestling to stop myself from landing a good blow on Tomasín's head with the text book I was holding, he suddenly said: "Do you play Monopoly? I feel like playing a game. Shall I get my Monopoly set?"

It was a relief to know that once in a while he could revert to being a child and the game he had in mind was, thank goodness, an innocent one.

"Alright," I agreed in desperation. "Later you can bring it and we'll have a game but *only* when you know these verbs."

Tomasín grimaced, blew an enormous bubble from the corner of his mouth and grudgingly turned his attention to the lesson. We struggled on in this way for two hours until the Latin master, Don

Federico, arrived to take over. I was glad of the break and it was good to know that I was not the only one whose unenviable task it was to instruct Tomasín.

Federico was a good-natured, well-built man in his mid forties. He smelt of tobacco and wine and walked with a strange bustling trot. His English was good though a little odd at times and he spoke it at every opportunity. I soon realised that he was an ardent fan of Shakespeare whose works he seemed to have studied in great detail in their original language. I found him a kindly and amusing character and we soon became friends.

"When we have finished with this young man I take you out for a drink," he said in English, as Tomasín searched for his Latin books. "I think you could do with one – no?"

"You can say that again!" I laughed. Tomasín, unable to understand, regarded us suspiciously with screwed-up eyes.

03 80

Walking out into the street in the middle of the day was like entering an oven but even the blazing sun seemed preferable to the gloom of the Vázquez house.

"Let's go to see!" said Federico. "Let's go to see this bar!"

He knew all the bars in Burgos and when he was not teaching, he could invariably be found in one or other of them. He particularly favoured the less reputable ones lurking in back streets, such as the Bar Paloma which we now entered. At this time of day it was filled exclusively with males with no woman to be seen anywhere. The men were drinking, laughing, swearing, spitting and playing dominoes. They all knew Federico and greeted him jovially, slapping him on the back and grinning at me over their raised glasses. At first I found all this a bit daunting but, after a few such jaunts with him, I had become used to it. As usual he ordered two glasses of white wine, downed his in one gulp and immediately suggested that we should leave. "I show you another place."

We threaded our way along the narrow pavement. A donkey brayed as it trotted past pulling a cart filled with vegetables. A few doors down from the Bar Paloma we drank more white wine before progressing to yet another of his haunts. I lost count of how many more we visited that morning but certainly my head was swimming by the time I got back to the house and I prayed fervently that my unseemly state would pass unnoticed in the Vázquez household. I climbed the stairs limply, keeping a firm grip on the banisters and trying to suppress my hiccups. By an act of will power I forced myself to walk steadily into the flat where I was vaguely aware of being greeted by Rosa.

"Ah señorita, thank goodness you are back. The lunch is ready and today you must hurry."

My legs felt as though they were about to buckle under me so I leaned against the wall for a minute. Rosa looked concerned.

"Are you alright señorita ? You are not ill?"

"No! no! " I said hurriedly, hoping my speech sounded normal. "I'm fine. It's just that I'm not used to this heat."

Rosa smiled. "Of course, I forgot. Yes, we are having a heat wave. You should not go out at this time of day. Anyway, you must have lunch and then prepare your things. The Señor and Señorito are leaving this afternoon for Santander and you are going with them. You will find it cooler there."

༄ ༄

We had left Burgos and the Castilian plateau far behind and were climbing high into the mountains. The road was bad and very narrow and Vázquez was not the best of drivers. We bumped along over the pot-holes and I closed my eyes as we negotiated each hairpin bend knowing how dangerously close we were to the edge with no barrier between us and a sheer drop. To make matters worse, ahead of us a bank of low cloud hung menacingly over the road. We entered it and were enveloped in a thick white mist, visibility reduced to nil. Vázquez leaned forward, straining to see the road ahead and guessing wildly at the bends. We slithered round them at a speed which seemed far from safe and I began to feel slightly sick. I turned round to see how Tomasín was reacting but he seemed totally unperturbed, his head buried in a comic.

So this is it, I thought. A dramatic way to end my short life! Then, suddenly, the mist cleared and I returned to sanity and was even able to appreciate the wild and beautiful mountain scenery. We reached a small whitewashed hostelry, its balcony bedecked with flowers and here we stopped briefly to refresh ourselves. We found a shady patio with a few tables and chairs and sat down to a *merienda* of hot chocolate and *churros*, a Spanish delicacy rather like long thin doughnuts, which we dipped in the chocolate. Vázquez's small, lecherous eyes gazed at me across the table as he sucked noisily at the *churros*.

"I hear you were out with Federico Suárez today," he remarked mopping his mouth with a napkin.

"That's right," I replied calmly, trying not to feel guilty. "We went for a walk before lunch."

"You shouldn't. The man's an alcoholic."

I felt like telling him that it was none of his business what I did with my spare time but thought better of it and said nothing. We got up to go back to the car and Vázquez sidled up to me and placed his hand on my bare arm. "I have to look after you, you know," he muttered in my ear, "while you're living in my house."

We continued our journey through the long summer afternoon until at last, as evening fell, we wound our way down the mountain slopes towards the coast and the town of Santander. The seafront was lined with colourful flower beds and palm trees spreading their fans against the evening sky. Behind them sparkled the blue-green waters of the Atlantic. Crowds of holidaymakers were taking their *paseo,* jostling and laughing. I felt the urge to hop out of the car and join them or run across the sands to splash in that inviting water. Vázquez must have read my thoughts for he said: "Tomorrow we shall bathe."

The *pensión* where the rest of the family was staying was a modest but comfortable establishment not far from the beach. Here I was introduced to Doña Constanza, Vázquez's wife, and his other children, three pretty girls and two small boys of three and four. The children clustered around me, grabbing at the presents I had brought them while the wife fixed me with an icy stare. She was a woman who might have been attractive but for the thick make-up which plastered her face. Her lips were painted to resemble the heart-shaped 'Hollywood' mouth fashionable with film stars but, unfortunately in her case, lack of skill had only succeeded in producing a blood-red sneer. Her voice was harsh and loud and her whole manner towards me hostile. Her instant dislike of me, which she made no attempt to hide, was totally reciprocated and I decided to have as little to do with her as possible.

That night I slept with the younger children and their nursemaid, Josefina, in one enormous room. Josefina was an attractive, rather plump girl with round, rosy cheeks and an infectious laugh. She adored the children and pandered to their every whim, a weakness they were not slow to exploit. The girls were lovely children and I got on well with them, but the two tiny boys were spoilt little monsters, a pair of mini-tyrants constantly pestering and demanding attention. Between them they made quite sure that Josefina did not have a minute's rest. I felt sorry for her and the following morning I helped her to get them washed, breakfasted and ready for the beach.

It was a warm, bright day and I was looking forward to having a dip in the sea so I donned my swimsuit, wearing it under my dress in readiness. It was a one-piece swimsuit. I had left my bikini back home in England because I knew that here, in Franco's Spain, such attire was not allowed. Wearing shorts in the streets was also frowned on and men couldn't wear swimming trunks – only swimming shorts. I found these petty, prudish rules quite absurd but woe betide anyone who did not observe them.

I set off with Josefina and the children for the beach to join the rest of the family. We found them sitting stiffly on wooden kitchen chairs which looked oddly out of place on the sand. Doña Constanza was surrounded by several of her friends. She embraced the younger children when we arrived but paid no attention to Josefina and me. Of the adults, only Vázquez was dressed for bathing, his large, hairy paunch bulging out over his swimming shorts. He was playing a ball game with Tomasín but they stopped as soon as we arrived and came over to join the group.

"How about a swim?" suggested Vázquez. "The water is good

this morning: warm and not too rough."

"Yes," I said. "That's just what I intend to do." I pulled off my dress and felt the warm sunshine and gentle sea breeze caressing my limbs. I turned and saw Vázquez standing, hands on hips, subjecting me yet again to his devouring gaze and beside him, Tomasín also staring and trying to suppress his sniggers. At the same time I was acutely aware of Doña Constanza's extreme disapproval. Suddenly I felt very angry. What have I done wrong? I asked myself. It's not my fault if her husband's a randy old so-and-so and her son is fast following in his footsteps! I turned away from them all and ran down towards the sea as fast as my legs could carry me. I plunged in, wishing the waves could take me away – far, far away from the whole lot of them.

For a few minutes I enjoyed the luxurious feeling of freedom, bobbing lightly up and down on the waves but this was all too short-lived for soon an ominous splashing behind me told me that I was no longer alone. To my dismay, I saw that both Vázquez and Tomasín had followed me into the water. Was there no escaping them? Tomasín soon joined me, splashing and diving and, when his father was not around, making comments about my legs. Vázquez, never far away, was plunging about like a demented hippopotamus. That lovely, relaxing swim which I had so looked forward to, had been ruined. I left the water and went to play with little Paquito and Miguel, trying to teach them a few English words while we built sand castles. I was well able to understand now why my predecessor, sensible girl, had spent so short a time with this family.

CB BD

It was nearly the end of August and I knew that all Spanish families return from their holidays promptly by the first of September. I therefore tried to avail myself as much as possible of the sun and sea although a lot of my time was spent giving the children lessons. In the afternoons I was instructed to go for walks with Tomasín and 'converse with him in English' which, of course, was easier said than done. We would walk along the cliffs and I would try him with a few simple sentences but Tomasín did not want to

17

practise English. He much preferred to ogle the girls sunbathing on the beach below. I asked him questions but he would answer in Spanish and I realised I was wasting my time. One afternoon I became so exasperated that I suddenly turned on him and yelled in English: "you cheeky, lazy little brat! I've had enough. I'm fed up with trying to teach you. At this rate you'll never learn English – not in a million years." He stared at me in surprise. "I don't understand you. I don't understand anything you say."

"Perhaps that's just as well!" I muttered.

The following Sunday, our last day in Santander, was a fiesta celebrated in true Spanish style with religious processions and dancing in the streets. In the afternoon, Vázquez, his wife and the older children went to the bullfight and I was left with Josefina and the monsters. They were being particularly boisterous and difficult and Josefina was beginning to flag so I suggested she should leave them with me that afternoon and have a couple of hours off. "You look as though you need it! I'll take them to the fun fair." Her face lit up.

"That would be wonderful! I could go and see Pepe. He's a boy I met here, but don't tell the Mistress!"

So I took the boys to the fun fair and spent a thoroughly exhausting afternoon chasing after them for they were here, there and everywhere, into everything and constantly demanding sweets, ices or rides. They were not used to being denied anything and threw terrible tantrums when they didn't get their own way. Poor Josefina! She certainly deserved her afternoon off and I hoped she was enjoying her secret rendez-vous with Pepe. For my part, somehow I managed to survive the afternoon and, even more miraculously, so did Paquito and Miguel.

When we got back to the *pensión*, Josefina had returned and was setting out clean clothes for the children. She was singing a little tune and looked flushed and happy.

"Had a good afternoon?" I enquired casually as I stripped the boys of their ice cream-covered shirts and shorts. She turned and smiled at me.

"Very good, señorita. Yes, it was very, very good. But please don't tell the Mistress!"

That evening we were joined at dinner by a friend of Vázquez, another doctor who worked at the same clinic. His name was Raúl García, a tall, handsome man in his thirties with gentle, brown eyes and a pleasant manner. He spoke quite good English and we chatted together during the meal. He asked me if I liked being in Spain, if I was happy with the job, etc. and I responded with all the expected polite answers. I could see, however, that he was not fooled and at the end of the meal he leaned over to me and said quietly: "I think you may be a little bored. Would you like to come out with me tonight? We could go dancing."

I looked across at Vázquez and his wife who were glaring at us, unable to understand our conversation, and I thought to myself, why not? Raúl García seemed courteous and pleasant and I had nothing else to do, so I agreed.

He took me to an open-air night club. The night was warm, the air full of the salty smell of the sea mixed with the perfume of flowers. Coloured lights twinkled in the trees and below them, people were dancing or sitting at tables drinking. On a small, raised dais a Latin-American band was playing a samba. We sat down at one of the tables and Raúl ordered *manzanilla*, a strong, white wine which I knew from my outings with Don Federico, had to be treated with respect.

"To our last night in Santander!" smiled Raúl, clinking his glass against mine. "And this is a pleasant way to spend it – is it not?" I agreed that it was and he replenished my half-empty glass.

A cabaret was now in progress. It consisted of a group of rather incompetent flamenco dancers and an unshaven guitarist. They strummed and clicked away and Raúl leaned back in his chair to watch them, tapping his foot and puffing at his cigarette. I finished my glass of *manzanilla* and he immediately re-filled it, ignoring my protests. By the time the cabaret ended I was beginning to feel slightly light-headed but somehow it didn't seem to matter. Through a pleasant haze I saw the dancers leave the dais and the band return. They struck up a lively cha-cha-cha and Raúl took me by the hand and led me onto the dance floor. For the first time since my arrival in Spain I was feeling quite relaxed and all my problems with the Vázquez family seemed to fade into insignificance. Between the dances my companion made sure my glass was never empty. By this time I had thrown caution to the winds because it was such a relief to find that I no longer cared whether or not Tomasín learnt English. I could not care less about the wretched boy, nor Don Tomás, nor Doña Constanza. I only knew that I was enjoying myself and that Raúl was a good dancer. As the night wore on I lost all sense of time. It was like being in a dreamy world of wine and music and Raúl. He was saying something to me but my bemused head couldn't take it in, being only aware that we were dancing a slow beguine and that I liked the smell of his after-shave. Then I realised that I was treading on his feet and finding it difficult to remain upright! The time had come to leave, I thought vaguely, as my head lolled against his shoulder.

"I think you have had a few glasses too many, little English girl," he was saying. I looked up at him. He smiled and I felt his lips touch my forehead.

"It's about time I took you home. I don't know what Tomás would think!"

"I wonder what your wife would think?" I said with sudden inspiration. We stopped dancing and walked back to the table in silence. Then he said: "How did you know? – that I'm married?"

"Call it feminine intuition," I yawned.

CB BO

"Wake up señorita! We have to get up early this morning."

Josefina's voice seemed unnaturally loud and grating. Surely it couldn't be time to get up already? I had only just gone to bed! Admittedly it had been three o'clock that morning when I had groped my way through the darkness between the sleeping children and fallen onto my bed in a drunken stupor. It was too cruel that now we had to get up *early*! I sat up and was immediately aware of my throbbing head and churning stomach. The room spun round and I sank back again on the pillow with a groan.

The thought of beginning another day was appalling but already there was feverish activity all around. Josefina was packing the children's things while Miguel and Paquito jumped on the beds and rushed screaming round the room. I looked at my watch. Six thirty.

After a cup of very strong coffee I could see more clearly but my head still ached as we drove to the bus station. As there was no room in Vázquez's car for all of us, it was decided that Josefina, Tomasín and I should return to Burgos by bus. It promised to be a hot day and already the early morning sun felt strong. At the bus station Vázquez gave me the tickets and money for our lunches and then departed. There were a lot of people milling around but I could not see anything resembling a bus.

"Hurry señorita or we shall not get a seat!" said Josefina. Following the direction of her waving hand I then noticed a heap of rusting metal in the shape of a large, ancient vehicle. It was probably older than the buses of the Hotel España and the Hotel Ávila and certainly in worse condition than either. I estimated that our chances of reaching Burgos in this contraption were, to say the least, remote.

We clambered up into our rickety seats with difficulty as all around us our fellow passengers were pushing and squeezing us back in their eagerness to find places. There were country folk with their inevitable crates of chickens, scruffy soldiers and spruce business men smelling of after-shave and cigars: an odd mixture of humanity. Still they kept pouring in and when all seats were filled, they just squeezed themselves into any remaining space until it was literally impossible for anyone to move. Last in was a civil guard, bristling with weapons and wearing the three-cornered hat that inspired such fear in my Basque friends. He sat on the floor by the door staring vacantly into space.

A few minutes later the driver arrived, a great hefty fellow with a red face and few teeth. He was wielding an enormous handle with which, after a series of unsuccessful attempts, he eventually succeeded in bringing the reluctant engine spluttering to life. Then he clambered over the passengers and shoe-horned himself into his seat.

Now, incredibly, we were moving, rocking to and fro, jolting and back-firing but at least moving. Once out on the open road the driver relaxed completely. With hands off the wheel, he lit endless cigarettes and chatted incessantly to the passengers around him, gesticulating enthusiastically as he did so. Above his head a large notice sternly reminded passengers that it was 'strictly forbidden to talk to the driver' and another forbade 'smoking and spitting in the coach'. From where I was sitting I could observe the speedometer and noticed that the top speed achieved was twenty kilometres per hour. By the time we started to climb into the hills it was incredibly hot and stuffy in the bus and we were all streaming with perspiration. Also the engine was over-heating and this meant that the driver had to stop every so often to lift the bonnet, inspect the engine, allow the radiator to cool and then pour in more water. This all took time. In addition, the driver seemed plagued by an unquenchable thirst and not a single way-side inn escaped his eagle eye. At every one we stopped and waited while he refreshed himself and by lunch time he was steering a somewhat erratic course. This was even worse than driving with Vázquez so I was thankful when at last we stopped to eat.

A mountain *fonda* provided us with a good meal but I was not hungry as my head was still pounding and my stomach protesting at the excesses of the night before. The combination of a hang-over and a long, hot journey in a rickety bus was hardly conducive to good appetite. However, Josefina and Tomasín tucked in heartily and were surprised at my indifference to the food.

Our journey was resumed but again progress was infuriatingly slow. It dawned on me that yet another reason for our all too frequent stops was that the bus carried mail. At every hamlet packets of letters were exchanged and this provided the driver with an excuse to chat with his many friends along the route. The procedure never varied. The bus would stop at a village and the driver sounded his horn. In the distance a figure would appear running towards us across the fields, bearing a packet of letters. He and the driver, after greeting each other like long-lost brothers, would exchange all the latest news and frequently retire to the local *fonda* for a drink.

In the meantime we, the passengers, had to remain suffering in the sweltering heat of the bus. The policeman guarding the doorway made sure that none of us alighted to stretch our legs. Here the driver was king and, of course, time for him was of no importance. None of the passengers complained. On the contrary, they seemed not in a hurry either and were quite contented gossiping and smoking. Apart from me, only the chickens, wilting in the sun, their beaks gaping open, their eyes glazed, seemed unhappy with the situation.

As we left the mountains the heat intensified and crossing the Castilian plateau was a nightmare. All around threshing was in progress and the choking dust hung like a cloud over the whole plain. By this time I was half fainting with heat and exhaustion and even Tomasín didn't look too well.

It was evening when we finally rattled into Burgos and we crawled out of the bus and staggered home. My head was splitting and I felt sick. Vázquez and the rest of the family had arrived home several hours earlier and were fresh and lively. By contrast all three of us were dusty, exhausted and in low spirits but Vázquez was far from sympathetic and Josefina was put to work immediately bathing and changing the children. Tomasín was sent to study until supper time and I was told to take the two younger boys for a walk when Josefina had prepared them. I told Vázquez that I was not feeling well, was going to bed and would not be having any supper. He was furious.

"There is nothing the matter with you." he shouted. "You will do as I say and take the children out!"

I replied firmly that I was tired after the journey, had a headache and was going to bed. Then I retired to my room ignoring his protests. A fine doctor! I thought, I wouldn't like to be one of his patients.

I undressed, had a shower, and got into bed, shivering with fever. A moment later there was a tap at the door and Rosa entered with a cup of cold camomile tea and an aspirin. She looked at me with some concern. "You are ill, señorita?"

I accepted the tea gratefully and gulped it down. "You have saved my life, Rosa. That journey nearly killed me."

"It's the heat," she assured me comfortingly.

I nodded. "Yes, that's right – the heat. You see we English just aren't used to it."

Rosa smiled understandingly and left the room. I was thankful that once again I had been able to use this excuse to cover up the ill effects of alcohol!

CHAPTER THREE

FRIENDS

Dr. Vázquez's wife, Doña Constanza, ruled her domestic staff with a rod of iron. All day long her raucous voice could be heard up and down the flat shrieking at the servants. "Rosa! Have you cleaned this room yet? Rosa! Where are my black shoes? Josefina! Why aren't the children ready? Rosa! *Rooooosa!*"

A cook had recently joined the household. Her name was Mercedes and she was a plump, motherly woman whose meals were delicious but Doña Constanza was always finding fault with her. She was late with the dinner, she had not gone shopping at the right time and *no*! That was *not* the fish that had been ordered. Rosa and Josefina were seemingly resigned to this bullying but the cook did not take to it so kindly. Although always respectful, she would sometimes attempt to defend herself and this would infuriate her mistress. Terrible rows ensued.

It was a relief to escape to the relative quiet of the conservatory where I gave Tomasín his lessons, but even there we could not always be free of Doña Constanza. Often, during the lessons, she would come in to dust her plants. As she polished each leaf she would watch me closely with a mixture of hostility and suspicion. This was unnerving, but I tried to take no notice of her. Vázquez also liked to watch the lessons when he could. One morning he came home early from the clinic. He was in a jovial mood for a change and stood observing us for some minutes. Then he sat down beside his son and remained there for the rest of the lesson.

"I see Tomasín is learning English well," he commented. "Now I wish you to give me lessons too."

From then on he insisted on having a class to himself every day before lunch. I rather resented this as it was not in our contract, but decided to put up with it for the sake of peace.

He was a more enthusiastic student than Tomasín but that did not make him any easier to teach. While above the table we were engaged in the idiosyncrasies of the English language, below it I was struggling to keep my knees away from his. His hands and feet also were often in an exploratory mood and this made concentration very difficult for both of us. On one memorable occasion we had just finished with the future tense and were about to start on the conditional when suddenly, and with the deftness of a magician, he produced a condom and dangled it before my astonished eyes.

"Do you know what this is?" he grinned. I nodded dumbly, too taken aback to say anything.

"I expect you thought you couldn't get them in Spain?" he enquired, chuckling under his breath. I looked at him coldly. "I hadn't thought about it," I replied truthfully.

"You see you can get them if you know where to go," he persisted, "on the black mark—"

"Lunch is ready," I interrupted him hastily. "Don't you hear the gong? We mustn't keep Doña Constanza waiting." The mention of his wife irritated him. He scowled and muttered: "Never mind *her*!"

I stood up and gathered the books together, anxious to get away from him.

"I think we ought to go," I insisted. "Oh, and perhaps you'd better put that away. I can hear Doña Constanza coming to fetch us for lunch."

Vázquez frowned ever more darkly and replaced the offending object in his pocket.

"Damn her!" he growled. "*I'm* the one who gives the orders in this house."

03 &0

Vázquez and his wife always ate alone at one end of the long table in the dining room. The servants ate in the kitchen and I had my meals with Josefina and the younger children in the nursery. This would have been a good arrangement but for the fact that the children's behaviour was appalling. If a meal met with their disapproval or they wanted the sweet course instead of the main one, they would fling their food on the floor in disgust and Josefina would then have to clear up the mess. I asked her why she put up with it but she only smiled and shrugged her shoulders. I was often tempted to try my hand at disciplining them and had to remind myself that, thankfully, this was not part of my job. However, I found a way of encouraging them to behave themselves for short periods by telling a story at every mealtime to be continued only if they were good. Most of the time this worked (to Josefina's delight) but not always.

Now that I had to teach Vázquez during the hour before lunch, I could no longer accompany Don Federico on his round of the bars. The family, particularly Doña Constanza, clearly disapproved of our innocent friendship. She hinted darkly that he was not a respectable person to be seen out with; he was an alcoholic with a bad reputation. "He has a wife in Navarre you know," she would say, "and a mistress in Burgos. Everyone knows that he has a mistress." I ignored her warnings, preferring to judge people by the way they treated me, and I had always found Don Federico both agreeable and kind. Moreover, what he did with his private life did not concern me and was certainly no business of theirs! I continued to see him in the evenings or on Sundays.

I greatly valued the hour or so of freedom which was mine in the evenings before supper for this was when I was able to meet up with Anita and her friends. I enjoyed being once more with people of my own age and all through the day I would look forward to eight o'clock when Anita would call for me and we would make for the Espolón to join the others. There were usually six of us: Anita, her best friend Marisol, three boys called Gonzalo, Sergio and Felipe – and me.

Marisol was a vivacious girl with dark eyes, shortish brown hair and a prettiness which stood on its own without the aid of make-up. Sergio was short and unusually fair for a Spaniard. It was easy to see that he had a great interest in Marisol for his eyes never left her and he was always trying to be close to her. She, for her part, managed skilfully to ignore all his attentions. Felipe was not in love with any girl but rather with the idea of becoming a bullfighter. It was an ambition that he knew full well would never be fulfilled but that did not prevent him from dreaming about it. He was totally obsessed and all his conversation was centred around bulls and various heroes of the ring whose exploits he followed with avid interest. Gonzalo wasn't in love with anyone or anything which was a relief. He was just a clown, a tall, lanky individual with huge glasses and an expression of permanent surprise. He had the ability to make anyone laugh at any time and it was impossible to feel low when he was around.

Sometimes we would sit in one of the pavement cafes in the Espolón and play cards or we would climb the steep hill behind the cathedral, wending our way between scrubby bushes and cypresses till we reached the little café at the top. This hill was known as the "Castillo" for it was here where the old castle once stood and some remains of it and its ancient walls could still be found among dense undergrowth.

The little café-bar at the top of the Castillo hill was small, friendly and primitive. There we would order a *porrón* of white wine and a dish of prawns. Sitting at one of the wooden tables in the cool of the evening, we would watch the setting sun glowing blood-red behind the tall cathedral spires. Far below us twinkled the lights of Burgos and beyond, the darkening plain stretched away into the distance.

Drinking from the *porrón* was a skill I had not yet mastered. It required holding it at arm's length and from that distance, pouring the wine accurately into one's mouth. Despite repeated efforts I usually made a mess of it, succeeding only in soaking myself with wine to the intense amusement of my companions. They, of course, were experts and usually came down the hill a good deal merrier than when we had climbed it, Anita and Marisol singing, Gonzalo dancing around, Felipe fighting imaginary bulls and Sergio trotting along behind Marisol like a faithful dog.

Sometimes we would call at Anita's house. It nestled snugly at the foot of the Castillo at the end of a dusty cul-de-sac on the outskirts of town. The house was small but detached with a pink tiled roof, cream walls and a tiny patio at the back. Inside, it was sparsely furnished with only the bare necessities but the atmosphere was so warm and hospitable that I felt very much at home there.

Anita lived with her Aunt Domi and one of her brothers, Teodoro, known to everyone as 'Teo'. Their small kitchen was usually packed with people – friends, neighbours, relatives – all talking at once, discussing the events of the day, laughing, joking or arguing in a friendly way – usually about politics. In the corner, by the charcoal stove, the diminutive figure of Aunt Domi could be distinguished hazily through the smoke and steam, busy with her frying pan. Every now and then she would add her own comments to whatever discussion was in progress, jabbing the air with her fork to emphasise certain points, her sharp, jet-black eyes darting from one speaker to another.

Between these debates Teo, sitting on the kitchen table and strumming away at his guitar, would entertain us with Latin American songs rendered in a rich, manly voice. It was not easy to leave that cosy haven and return to the Vázquez flat. I felt a bit like a prisoner whose parole had come to an end.

Best of all were Sundays when I had the whole day off and could go with my friends on outings into the countryside. The first of these was an exciting experience, a picnic which was organised soon after my return from Santander. We gathered at Anita's house bright and early on a hot September morning. There were ten of us as our usual group had been joined by Anita's older brother, Pablo, who was a medical student living at the local hospital. Also there were two ex-college friends of Anita's and a French boy called Michel who was spending the summer holidays in Spain. Marisol was learning French and was happy to practise it with Michel who was rather good-looking.

When I arrived Aunt Domi was packing an enormous picnic into bags and rucksacks aided by Anita and her friend Mari Carmen. Michel and Marisol were deep in conversation and Sergio was watching them sulkily. He was the only one who didn't seem happy that morning. We each grabbed a bag of food and Teo slung his inseperable guitar over his shoulder. Now we were all set to go.

We strode off across the fields, following the river and singing as we went to the accompaniment of the guitar and Michel's mouth organ. The sun, rising higher in the sky, gained strength, beating down on us as we tramped across the treeless plain. From time to time we stopped to quench our thirst with wine from a *bota*, a round container made of hide which, when squeezed at arm's length, squirted a jet of its contents into the mouth. It was slightly easier than a *porrón* and, driven by necessity, I managed to master it to some extent.

As I walked along beside Anita, I recounted my adventures in Santander. She seemed surprised. "You went out with that older man?" she exclaimed in disbelief. "To a *nightclub* on your own?"

"Yes, why not?"

"I wouldn't do *that*. In Spain girls don't do that sort of thing."

"How old-fashioned! Everything here is so behind the times."

Anita regarded me with disapproval mixed with admiration. "I think things must be very different in England," she mused.

I thought it best to end this discussion so I asked her about her parents and almost immediately regretted having done so as I saw her smile fade.

"My parents are both dead. My father was a university teacher and he was killed by the Falangists in the Civil War. I can't remember him. I was very tiny."

"That's terrible," I exclaimed. "Your father killed!"

"So were my uncles although one of them managed to escape to France. You see," here she instinctively lowered her voice, "we are Republicans. My father and uncles were shot and my grandfather was imprisoned." There was a pause while I tried to take in this horrifying revelation. Then I said: "And your mother?"

"They took away our house and all our possessions. She fled with us three children but there was nowhere for her to go so Aunt Domi took us all into her house. She's my father's sister. My mother had a weak heart and the stress of it all was too much for her. She died a few years ago. Poor Mamá."

I put my arm round her shoulders. "I'm so sorry," I said.

"Perhaps you'd rather not talk about it." She shook her head. "No, it's alright, I don't mind. We're not the only ones. Nearly everyone lost relatives in the Civil War and we're lucky really. Aunt Domi is very good to us. She is paying for my brothers' careers: Pablo wants to be a doctor and Teo is studying law. It's just that we have to be very careful. They know about our political past and that doesn't make life easy for us."

Again the ominous 'they'; it reminded me of my conversation with the Basques on the train and I felt very sorry for Anita.

By this time we had caught up with the others who had gone ahead and were now sitting on the river bank under a poplar tree. They were watching a gypsy boy on the opposite bank weaving a basket from reeds. Marisol was still practising her French and seemed to be enjoying a joke with Michel who kept murmuring his musical language into her ear, studying her face with his golden-brown eyes. She responded with little peals of laughter, cheeks pink with pleasure.

Sergio was leaning against the tree, eyes downcast, kicking irritably at the grass and occasionally throwing a sullen glance in the direction of the happy pair. As I approached he grabbed me by the arm. "Do you understand French?" he muttered angrily, "What are those two saying? What's he saying to her?"

"I'm sorry Sergio, I can't help you. My French is dreadful and they're speaking too fast for me to follow."

Sergio sighed gloomily, plunging his hands deep into his pockets. "Since that Michel arrived she's spent all her time with him," he complained.

"Oh come on Sergio! Forget them! Marisol's only practising her French."

"I hope you're right. I hope that's all she's practising with him. What does she see in him anyway?"

I smiled. "Well, he's a really nice boy."

Sergio muttered something inaudible under his breath and stalked away.

We set off again and walked for about an hour until we reached a spot which everyone agreed would be ideal for our picnic. It was on a river bank under a small grove of trees at the foot of a hill. Perched on top was a small village with mud-coloured houses reminding me of the ones I had seen from the train. Here we set up our camp and three of the lads went off to explore the village. They returned shortly bearing bottles filled with water from the communal fountain and a collection of beakers, knives, cooking pots and various other utensils borrowed from the obliging village priest. It was not long before we were tucking into a giant bowl of salad with hunks of bread and slices of Aunt Domi's tortilla, all washed down with generous quantities of wine.

While we were eating we heard the jingling of sheep bells and a few nervous, woolly heads peered at us between the bushes. Then the shepherd appeared, a young boy dressed in skins and rope-soled sandals. He reminded me of an illustration in a book of Bible stories I had as a child which showed the boy David preparing to face Goliath.

The shepherd said nothing but came and stood at a short distance, watching us expectantly as we ate – rather like a hungry dog waiting patiently for scraps to be thrown its way. Anita cut a large piece of bread and a good portion of tortilla and held it out to him in silence. He ran forward, a stick-like arm protruding from the skins, and snatched the food eagerly. The next moment he was gone and his sheep with him.

"Poor lad!" I commented. "He must be hungry."

Anita nodded solemnly. "Lots of people are hungry here."

The meal over, we all felt replete and perhaps a little guilty after what we had just witnessed. The wine was making us sleepy so we stretched out under the trees to while away the hottest part of the day in their generous shade. Teo strummed gently on his guitar while José and Mari Carmen danced languidly together with bare feet. Michel had fallen asleep and Sergio, swift to take advantage of this happy state of affairs, was trying to persuade Marisol to dance. She was not enthusiastic about the idea, preferring to read a magazine. Gonzalo had climbed a tree and was amusing himself aiming small pebbles at the recumbent bodies below.

I lay back on the dry, wispy grass and closed my eyes, hoping I would not be a target for one of Gonzalo's pebbles. I turned over in my mind what Anita had told me, horrified by the revelation that her life had already been marred by so much violence and tragedy. I knew little about politics generally and far less about Spanish politics but already several things were becoming clear. It was obvious, even after so many years, that the dark shadow of the Civil War still lingered over Spain. There were reminders of it everywhere: in the ruined buildings, the poverty and, above all, the bitterness of a divided people. I could see that its aftermath was still affecting people's everyday lives and that this was a land over which hung a blanket of fear.

My reveries were interrupted by something tickling my face. I opened my eyes to see Teo holding a long blade of grass. "Wake up!" he grinned. "I want to show you something funny."

I sat up and followed his pointing finger. A herd of cows was ambling towards us and Felipe was attempting to lure one of them into combat with his jacket. He stood in front of it, flapping wildly and making encouraging noises. "*Eh toro! eh! eh!*" The animal stared back at him contemptuously, chewing the cud and flicking flies from its haunches, totally unimpressed. Everyone was laughing and Felipe eventually gave up, flinging his jacket on the ground in disgust.

"You'll never make a bullfighter!" teased Pablo. Suddenly the cow twitched, and turning, careered straight towards Felipe who was walking back to our group. "Look out *torero!*" yelled José. Mari Carmen screamed and Felipe ran. I had never seen anyone run so fast, but the cow galloped past him followed by all the others in a frenzied stampede. Felipe tripped and fell into the dust while, from the tree, came the sound of Gonzalo's guffaws. "I couldn't resist it!" he hooted. "It was a good shot. Right on the haunches!" He was holding a pebble between finger and thumb and rocking so much with laughter I was afraid he might fall out of the tree. Felipe, who had got up and was dusting himself down, rushed towards the tree, blazing with anger. Anita ran over to calm him and Gonzalo climbed up further.

As the day started to cool, we all became more active. Some of the boys went for a swim in the river while the rest of us hunted for sticks to make a fire. We melted chocolate in one of the priest's cooking pots until it was ready to pour into cups and eat with biscuits. Later we gathered everything together and walked up the hill to the village to return what we had borrowed. There was not a great deal to see in the village: just a church, an inn and a few houses clustered around the fountain. The paths between the houses were covered with slippery white straw among which a number of chickens were scratching and pecking. Beside the fountain several women had gathered with their water jugs, gossiping and laughing. Children played around in the dirt and watching them on a bench outside the inn was an incredibly aged man, perhaps the oldest inhabitant, enjoying the evening sun. He treated us to a toothless grin as we passed.

We could not stay long in the village as it was getting late. We had a lengthy trek ahead of us and we wanted to get home before nightfall. However, it was not to be, for the sun was already going down as we set off and soon we were walking back in darkness. Carefully, by moonlight, we picked our way across the fields, (I slightly nervously as Teo had warned me there might be snakes) till at last we reached the bridge and arrived under the floodlit cathedral. My friends accompanied me to the doorway of the Vázquez house and there we parted.

I could not bring myself to climb those stairs immediately but paused to watch them all disappearing down the street. I could see that Felipe was pointing excitedly at a poster advertising next Sunday's bullfight and, as they rounded the corner, Sergio was trying to hold Marisol's hand. I sighed and reluctantly made my way up the stairs, the sound of their youthful laughter still ringing in my ears.

CHAPTER FOUR

HAZARDS

Tomasín was absent-mindedly drawing something that resembled a well-endowed female on the corner of his exercise book while I explained to him about collective nouns. Outside, a violent storm was raging. Thunder roared, rain lashed against the glass of the conservatory and the silent canary huddled miserably in its cage. Suddenly, the boy looked up and pointed across the room.

"See how the lightning has lit up father's study!" he exclaimed. "But that's funny! – there are no windows in that room."

Sure enough a sinister bright light was flickering behind the glass panel which divided Vázquez's study from the dining room. With a gasp of horror I leapt to my feet. "Quick Tomasín! the study is on fire!"

Smoke was billowing from the study door as we rushed towards it. Don Tomás's projection screen, stored in a corner, was blazing away merrily but the flames had nearly finished with that and were now eagerly devouring the many books lining the walls. Doña Constanza had also become aware of the disaster and was shrieking and screaming at the servants at the top of her voice. "Rooosa! Josefina! The house is on fire. Quickly, quickly bring water Roooosa!"

Everyone was now coughing and spluttering from the smoke and pandemonium reigned. Tomasín and I tried to beat out the flames that were spreading over the carpet while Josefina and Rosa hurled buckets of water at the books. They rushed frenziedly back and forth from the kitchen bumping into each other in their panic and spilling much of the precious water. Doña Constanza directed operations, screaming and flinging her arms about. In the hall, holding their father's lighter, Miguel and Paquito stood watching the chaotic scene with expressions of profound satisfaction with a job well done.

At last the flames were extinguished and we were able to survey the damage which was considerable. The screen and many of Vázquez's medical books had been destroyed, the walls were blackened and there were holes in the carpet. I wondered how Doña Constanza would deal with her younger offspring who had deliberately set fire to the house but to my astonishment, they were not even reprimanded. All she said was: "Oh dear! What a mess! Tomás shouldn't leave his lighter on the desk!" I came to the conclusion that life in the Vázquez household was hazardous indeed − and in more ways than one. This suspicion was confirmed a few nights later.

ભ ૪

It had been a glorious day. Being Sunday, I had spent my free afternoon with Don Federico, climbing the steep, tree-lined road to the monastery. The day was warm and fine, the former oppressive heat having diminished since the thunder-storm and this being late September, there was the faintest hint of autumn in the air.

As we walked, Federico told me stories of his experiences in the Civil War and of his native province of Navarre. We talked about the Festival of San Fermín in Pamplona when bulls were let loose in the streets on their way to the ring, the young men running before them to test their courage. Federico assured me that he himself had often participated in this dangerous activity as a younger man and had various scars to prove it.

"Life in Navarre is much better than here in Castile. The people are livelier. Have you seen the *jota* danced? And the countryside is good − we have mountains and green grass. You must visit Navarre. The wine is wonderful."

I wondered why he had left it to live in Burgos and was about to ask him when I suddenly remembered what Doña Constanza had said and decided it would be wiser not to.

We came upon the monastery, standing lonely and dignified in the parched landscape. This was a self-sufficient community of Trappist monks, vowed to silence, who apart from farming their land, also made a fine liqueur for which they had a good reputation in the district.

"Let's go to see these monks," said Don Federico. "We buy a bottle of their liqueur."

So saying, he led the way across a cobbled courtyard to a great studded door on the far side. In response to his knock the door was opened by a tall young man in a brown habit and rope-soled sandals. It was amusing to watch the two of them negotiating, Federico jovial and chatty, the monk silent and serious, communicating only with gestures of the head and hands. At last we came away with the bottle of liqueur, this being the object of Federico's visit, but not before making a brief tour of the church the interior of which was surprisingly magnificent. The statues and rich carvings were beautiful enough but these were as nothing compared with the lavish splendour of the reredos ablaze with gold and glittering with jewels. Could this, I wondered, have once been part of the fabled Inca treasure which was supposed to have found its way into so many Spanish churches? There was no time to ponder this intriguing possibility because Federico was saying: "Come! that is beautiful but I am thirsty. You also? Let's go to see my friends in the bar Gaona!"

ඃ ෴

I must have been sleeping for some time for I had gone to bed early that night. Certainly I had been dreaming and my head was still full of Atahualpa and his gold when I suddenly awoke. Something must have disturbed me for I was not a fitful sleeper, – but what?

The night was fine so I had left the shutters and blinds open. A gentle breeze stirred the curtains and the room was bathed in silvery moonlight. I looked around but saw nothing unusual. Then there was a faint rattling coming from the door. I saw the handle turn to the side, remaining there for a few seconds before returning to its original position. Was I dreaming still? But no, the same thing happened again and this time, little by little, the door started to open. The figure of someone in a dressing gown framed in the doorway, stood peering in and from its short lumpy shape, I knew at once who it was.

For a few seconds I lay there, paralysed, like a rabbit being stalked by a predator. Then I came to my senses and as my visitor crept stealthily across the room, I called out: "Don Tomás! What are you doing here?"

"Hush!" he responded in a muffled voice. "I heard your shutters swinging. They should be closed." He walked over to the window and started fumbling with the shutters.

"Leave them!" I said, sitting up in bed, pulling the covers about me. "I like them open. Now please go!"

It was quite obvious that Vázquez had no intention of leaving. He came over to the bed and sat on it, breathing heavily and muttering something inaudible. Help! I thought, desperately, he's so confident of his right to my bed that he won't even wait for an invitation!

"You are so young, so *guapa*!" he breathed, his small eyes gleaming with excitement.

"Get out at once or I shall scream and wake everyone."

"You don't mean that." He leaned over me with a twisted smile and I felt his podgy hand on my bare neck. I shrank away from him, sickened by his persistence.

"You will see that I am not joking if you don't leave this room instantly. You should be ashamed of yourself. What would Doña Constanza think?"

At the mention of his wife he drew back a little but quickly rallied. "Oh you don't need to worry about my wife, she's asleep; sleeps like a log. She won't know anything about it."

"You disgust me Don Tomás. Is this the way Spanish husbands behave? Tomorrow I shall tell your wife exactly what you get up to while she's asleep."

At this Vázquez recoiled as effectively as if I had struck him a physical blow. "You must be mad," he spluttered. In an instant his mood changed from lustful desire to blind rage. He grabbed me roughly by the shoulders.

"You will tell her nothing! Do you hear me?" he hissed between clenched teeth, his face close to mine. "You will tell her nothing at all about this!"

"I promise you, Don Tomás," I said looking steadily back into his eyes and trying to keep my voice calm, "that if you don't get out of this room right now your wife will be the first to know in the morning."

That did it. He rose to his feet and stalked away, muttering furiously under his breath. Happily, I was not yet familiar with all the stronger expletives of the Spanish language! The door closed and immediately I leapt up and turned the key in the lock; then I leaned against it, breathless, my heart still pounding, but relieved beyond measure to be rid of my unwelcome visitor. What a fool I had been not to realise that all his previous overtures had been leading up to this! I could have kicked myself for being so naïve. I glanced up at the sorrowful Madonna above my bed, just visible in the moonlight, hoping she was not too offended by the sordid little drama that had just taken place so incongruously in her presence.

For some days after this incident Vázquez was not in a good mood. My attitude to him was the same, as I thought it best to act as though nothing had happened. I assumed that, having made it abundantly clear that I did not consider my duties as an English teacher should include nocturnal romps in the bedroom, the whole episode would blow over and be forgotten. Nevertheless I took the precaution of locking my bedroom door and this was as well because, a few nights later, I was again woken by the handle turning. This happened on several occasions and I could not help marvelling, as I listened to his retreating footsteps, at the obstinacy and vanity of the man. He apparently was convinced that it could only be a matter of time before I fell victim to his persistence and presumably, in common with many of his fellow countrymen, he was under the impression that all foreign girls were easy prey, willing if not eager to hop into bed with anyone at any time. His bitter disappointment showed itself in a sullen and resentful manner towards me that had not been there before. No wonder, I thought, *no wonder* that other English girl had gone so soon!

Fortunately, about this time, Vázquez and his wife left for a holiday in Portugal and with their departure, life became pleasanter for a short while. For a start, I was able to resume my midday outings with Don Federico which I enjoyed for two reasons: firstly, because I found his company agreeable and amusing and secondly, because he knew a great many people and through him I had been able to make several new friends.

One morning, after Tomasín's Latin lesson, Don Federico announced that he was going to show me his academy. Now, I was very intrigued to see this place for he had often mentioned it, saying that he taught a variety of subjects there, such as English, Latin, and even touch-typing and that he had a large number of pupils. In my mind's eye, I had formed a mental picture of this academy. I imagined it as a dignified place of learning, perhaps a large airy studio well equipped with books and desks, the rows of orderly students sitting in rapt attention while Professor Don Federico expounded the virtues and complexities of Shakespearian English.

"So where is it, Federico?" I enquired as we walked down the stairs and out into the street.

"Ah!" You will see, you will see," he replied with an air of mystery.

After walking for some time, I realised that we were not going anywhere new but were making for his usual haunt, a tumble-down district in the old part of the town. In fact, we were now entering that mean little street that was home to so many of his favourite bars. Purposefully, Federico trotted along but, near the end of the street, he stopped.

"Please, this way," he said and with a sweeping gesture, indicated a small, dark and rather smelly doorway lurking along-side the entrance to the Bar Paloma.

We climbed a rickety staircase which led to a series of decaying and, as was evident from the many holes in the stairs, rat-infested tenements. On the first landing, a small window revealed an inner courtyard – a scene of unrelieved squalor. Numerous children, ragged, dirty and barefoot were playing among the rubbish in the yard while a mountainous woman was attempting to calm a screaming infant and peg out washing at the same time. Two scrawny cats were having a disagreement in one corner of the yard. They crouched behind the rubbish piles, ears back, their malevolent wails accompanying those of the baby in a bizarre trio. The rancid smell of frying pork fat drifted upwards through a gaping crack in the window.

On the second landing, Federico flung open a door to reveal a shabby little room, dusty and bare save for a few rickety chairs and a small table with an ancient typewriter. A grimy window overlooked the street. I glanced at him uncertainly.

"Is this it?"

"Yes," he beamed, glowing with pride. "It is very good. You like it?"

"Oh yes, of course, it's great!"

I tried to stifle my disappointment. Little did I know as I stood there surveying the bleakness of Federico's 'academy', that before long, it was to become the setting for some of the most exciting moments of my life.

CHAPTER FIVE

PUCK'S SPELL

I had always wanted to learn typing. I guessed it could be very useful to me when I returned to London. Don Federico told me he had gained a diploma in speed typing in the United States and I knew I would not find a better teacher, so we came to an arrangement. He would teach me typing and in return, I would help him to give English classes to his advanced students in the evenings.

As Vázquez was still away, I was able to go to Federico's academy for my lessons during my free hour before lunch. I was shown the fingering for the different keys and was made to practise various exercises while Federico nipped down below for a quick *chato* in the Bar Paloma. He would soon return, however, and stand behind me as I typed, viewing my efforts with a critical eye and rolling a cigarette in the pocket of his jacket. This little trick of his never ceased to amaze me. He always kept black tobacco and cigarette papers in his pocket and when he felt like a smoke, he would just put in his hand, twirl it around a bit and – hey presto! There was a perfect cigarette. One quick lick and it was ready for use.

"That is really very clever Federico," I said to him one morning. "How do you do it so quickly?"

"Maybe I will teach you, but first you must learn to type."

"Dr. Vázquez is coming home next week and I don't know whether he will let me come any more," I sighed. "Sometimes I get so fed up with those people. The children are totally out of control. You know they even tried to set fire to the house the other day?" Don Federico raised his eyebrows. "No!"

"Yes, and what's more, their mother said nothing at all to them about it. It's so dangerous! I'm afraid I would have tried to teach them a lesson if they had been my children."

"Ah – we must not punish these little innocents," smiled Federico, tongue in cheek. "You know – *the quality of mercy is not strained, It droppeth as the gentle rains from heaven.*' Portia, Merchant of Venice. You know that? So beautiful!"

Don Federico was an enthusiastic student of The Bard. He knew many long passages from Shakespeare's works and would frequently quote them.

"Oh, you are too soft-hearted, Freddie! Anyway, it's not only the children, it's the whole atmosphere of the place that bothers me. The servants don't seem very happy either. Doña Constanza shouts at them all the time."

"*Thou seest we are not alone unhappy. This wide and universal theatre presents more woeful pageants than the scene wherein we play.*" As you Like it, Act II. Such a wonderful poet, your Shakespeare!"

Don Federico studied the page I had been typing, puffing at his cigarette.

"Yes, that is quite good but try to keep it all more even. You see how some letters they are weaker than others? That is not good. Now practise this exercise – fill the whole page! I am just going out for a few minutes, I will not be long. Just a quick *chato*."

He left me and I set to work on my exercise. A few minutes later I heard the sound of double footsteps on the stairs. Who would be coming to Don Federico's academy at this hour? Could it be Vázquez and his wife, home early, and coming to drag me away? No, I told myself. That was ridiculous.

Then there was the sound of male voices on the landing outside, the door opened and in walked two good-looking young men. The first was tall and very dark with jet-black hair and thick eyebrows that nearly met in the middle. His skin was tanned a deep mahogany in striking contrast to his white open-neck shirt and flashing smile. Wow! I thought, admiring his Moorish good looks, this is an improvement on what I had imagined!

Then I noticed his companion standing just behind him in the shadow of the doorway and I was instantly transfixed. Never before had I come across anyone to whom I felt so immediately attracted. He was tall and slim with gently waving dark hair and sideburns and what seemed to me an incredibly handsome face. Under arching eyebrows, his eyes were an amazing emerald green with thick black lashes. He looked rather pale, in spite of a sun tan, and had about him a certain air of reticence. One look at him was quite enough to make me feel weak at the knees! In fact the effect he had on me from that first moment can only be described as electrifying. I caught my breath as, quite suddenly, I was overcome by a feeling of intense excitement. This is absurd, I told myself, trying to control the adrenalin which my heart was feverishly pumping around, I don't even know him! He's a complete stranger. But alas, it was no use. Federico's obsession with Shakespeare must have evoked the spirit of Puck and the mischievous sprite had dropped some of his charmed potion into my eyes at the precise moment this individual had walked through the door – and I was lost! There could be no other explanation.

"*Buenos días, señorita*," said the dark one regarding me with a mixture of amusement and surprise. "We are looking for Don Federico Suárez."

"Oh... oh yes," I stuttered, still in a bemused state. "Don Federico isn't here at the moment, he went out. You might find him in the Bar Paloma."

He laughed. "That's very likely. He's sure to be in one of the bars. We'd better go and look for him."

"But he said he'd he back directly," I said, desperate to keep them there a bit longer.

"In that case perhaps we'll wait for him – that's if you don't mind."

"Oh no, I don't mind at all," I assured him.

The dark one looked me up and down with some curiosity. "You're foreign, aren't you?"

"Yes, English. Don Federico is teaching me typing."

I saw that the green-eyed one was also looking at me with interest and I felt the blood rushing to my cheeks – much to my acute embarrassment as I was not in the habit of blushing.

The dark one was holding something that looked like a child's toy. Anxious to make conversation, I pointed to it and said: "What's that?"

"A frog," was the reply. "A clockwork frog. Look!"

He wound the thing up and set it down carefully. We watched it hop erratically across the dusty floor till it collided with the wall opposite and lay whirring on its back.

"It's a nice toy but don't you think you're a little old for things like that?" I joked, glancing at the green-eyed one who smiled at me, looking even more handsome. My knees grew ever weaker. The dark one was laughing.

"It's for my nephew," he was saying, "he's two tomorrow. But I can see you like it, so here – it's yours!"

He tossed it to me, then turned to his friend. "Come on, Luis, we'd better go and look for Federico downstairs in the Paloma. He might be hours."

So, I thought, now I know his name: Luis. That's something, anyway. They said goodbye and were gone and I was left holding the frog and wondering what had happened to me.

I listened to them walking down the stairs then rushed to the window and looked out into the street below. I watched them emerge from the entrance then, almost at once, disappear again into the Bar Paloma. I waited and watched, longing to see him again and soon my patience was rewarded for all three of them re-appeared and stood talking for some time on the pavement. As the window was jammed shut I could not hear what was being said which was frustrating. I gazed at Luis and wished I could see more than the top of his head. His friend seemed to dominate the conversation and Luis hardly spoke at all. At last Federico slapped them both heartily on the back and vanished. I watched them walking away down the street and at the same time, heard Federico's footsteps climbing the stairs. He bustled into the room.

"Ah, I am sorry I have been so long. Come, let us go down and have a *chato* together. Have you finished the exercise? No you have not. That is bad. You have done nothing. But never mind, we go to have a *chato*."

We went down to the Bar Paloma, pushing our way through the groups of drinking men, the gamblers and the table-football players, to the bar. Around us the men's berets bobbed in time to their animated conversation, and the blind lottery ticket sellers could be heard singing out their numbers. "*Para hoy! Para hoy!* Today's draw. Buy and you will win the fat one!"

The room was thick with the haze of tobacco and the floor was littered with rubbish: seafood shells, scraps of food, screwed-up paper, cigarette ends and spittle. Everything was thrown on the floor and cleared up periodically by a boy with a huge broom. At first I had been reluctant to throw things around like this, inhibited as I was by early training in tidiness but after a few weeks in Spain, I had learnt to conform. Don Federico ordered white wine and prawns which we ate with our fingers, casting the shells on the floor to join the piles lying at our feet.

"Freddie," I began, sipping my wine, "Freddie dear, who is he? I mean who are they?"

He looked at me in surprise. "Who is who?"

"Those two young men who came to see you just now."

"Oh, them!" Don Federico took a swig of his wine. "That was Paco, Él de La Morena. Is a nice lad. Came with a message from his mother – that's La Morena, who has the restaurant on the other side of the river. Best restaurant in town. I know her well, for many years, since the war. She was a beautiful woman." He smiled thoughtfully as he remembered. "When she was young she was so beautiful! Very dark. That is why they call her *La Morena*. She is like a gypsy!"

Now I recalled having heard people talk of the Bar-Restaurante La Morena, and the raven-haired woman who ran it, a widow renowned, apparently, not only for her ravishing beauty but also for the superb quality of her cuisine.

"So that's the son of La Morena," I mused. "No wonder he's so handsome! But Freddie, how about the *other* one, the one called Luis?"

"Oh him," Federico dismissed him with a wave of the hand. "Oh, that's just a buddy of Paco's." Having spent some time in the States, Federico often used quaint American expressions when he spoke English. "Just a buddy. He wants to learn typing so maybe I teach him."

This sounded very promising. I decided to take the bull by the horns and confide in my friend.

"Freddie, I would like to see him again."

He raised his eyebrows slightly as he placed one of the self-rolled cigarettes in his mouth. "Why?" he asked, lighting it. "You like that boy?"

I nodded. "Yes, I do, and I would like to get to know him."

"I see," said Federico, smiling indulgently. "Well, that should be not too difficult. I'm giving him his lessons right after yours."

ଓ ଞୁ

Love at first sight indeed! This sort of thing only happened in books and romantic films and in plays like "Romeo and Juliet". It was all absolute nonsense; at least, that is what I had always believed. But now it was happening to *me* of all people. I, who had always prided myself on being thoroughly practical and down-to-earth. It was so annoying! For here I was in this pathetic state and mine was a very extreme case with the severest symptoms, probably incurable. I could think of nothing but Luís all day long and even at night the torment continued because he monopolised my dreams. I became highly absent-minded and during Tomasín's lessons, the teacher was now finding it as hard to concentrate as the pupil. I kept thinking about that pale face and those amazing green eyes. It was terrible.

At first Luis would arrive at Don Federico's academy for his lesson just as I was leaving and this was agony. However, one day Federico suggested that we should both join him for a quick drink between the lessons. Federico would talk and Luis would listen and I would watch Luis listening to Federico talking. There was little actual communication between Luis and me and I had the impression that he was a very shy person. Nevertheless one day I noticed that he arrived for his lesson ten minutes early. He sat on one of the rickety chairs watching me and I made a great number of typing errors.

The next time he arrived fifteen minutes early and Don Federico, who was a perceptive person, suddenly made a suggestion.

"Look, why don't I give you two lessons together? You could take it in turns to type. It would save me time too. At this hour I am so busy – I have so many people I have to see in the Bar Paloma. Business matters, you understand. Would you mind?"

"Oh no! *I* wouldn't mind," I said glancing anxiously at Luis. To my delight he smiled and said that would be fine.

℃ ℬ

Never had lessons been so blissful. Afterwards we would accompany Don Federico on his lunchtime round of the bars and one day, not long afterwards, came the chance I had been waiting for so impatiently. We were drinking in the Paloma, when Don Federico suddenly looked at his watch.

"*Hombre!* You two must excuse me for I have to go to see somebody in the Bar Ávila. It is very important and I am late, so goodbye. I will see you tomorrow."

He drained. his glass and trotted out of the bar muttering, "I am late. I am late," like the White Rabbit in Alice in Wonderland. Dearest Federico, I thought to myself, what a good friend I had in him! Now, at last, I was alone with the object of my infatuation.

"Shall we go somewhere else?" suggested Luis. "It's very hot in here and I know another place which is not so crowded."

We left the Paloma and walked down the street together. I felt flustered and excited and stupidly, could think of nothing to say to him. We entered another bar and sat down at one of the tables. Luis ordered drinks and lit a cigarette. I could see that he too was nervous. I asked him what he did and he told me he was a medical student but his studies had been interrupted by illness. He would soon be taking them up again at Madrid University. I asked him about his family.

"There are five of us. I live with my three brothers and my mother, near the river at the other end of town."

I noticed he did not mention his father but by this time I had learned that it was not tactful to ask people about their fathers, so I said nothing. However, after a short pause he volunteered.

"My father was a captain in the Republican army." My worst

fears were confirmed as he added, "they killed him at the time of the Civil War."

"Th... they?"

He nodded, grimly stubbing out his cigarette. "When they took control of Burgos."

He glanced over his shoulder and looked about him in that characteristic way which had become so familiar to me and to my astonishment, I found I was now doing the same. Fear, it seemed, was infectious.

Luis stood up. "Let's sit at that table over there, away from everybody," he said. We moved to a table in the corner and sat down again.

"You can't be too careful," he explained. "You see, sometimes they go around in plain clothes. You can't trust anyone. Anyway," he lowered his voice almost to a whisper. "It was terrible what they did to my father. Soon after they took control of Burgos they called at our house. It was in the daytime and we were having a meal. They grabbed my father and dragged him down into the street. My mother was screaming and we were all crying and then they shot him right there in front of the house, in front of us all and left his body on the pavement. I was very little but I remember it so clearly."

I shuddered as I tried to imagine the dreadful scene.

"I don't know what to say, Luis. That's a terrible story."

He gave a cynical laugh. "You will hear many such stories and some of them worse than mine. But that's enough of me. Tell me about yourself. What are you doing here in Spain, anyway?"

I told him about my job, about the difficult family I was with and the problems of teaching Tomasín. He laughed and I could see that he was gradually unwinding, becoming less tense. I wished that we could go on chatting for ever but it was late and I knew they would be waiting for me at the Vázquez house.

"I'll have to go," I said reluctantly, "or I'll be late."

"I'll walk back with you."

At the doorway of the house we said goodbye and I was just about to climb the stairs when suddenly he hurried after me and caught me by the arm.

49

"Listen! I've been wanting to ask you out for a long time. Would you... that is, are you... doing anything this evening?"

"No," I replied hardly able to believe me ears.

"Could we meet then?"

"Why not?" My heart was beating insanely fast.

"I'll see you here at eight then. *Hasta luego!*"

I staggered up the stairs in a sort of dream. It was all too good to be true.

cઉ ชა

That evening I spent a considerable time on my appearance. Victory was within my grasp and I was going to pull out all the stops. He arrived promptly at the appointed time and we walked to the Espolón. We did not stay there long because he said he didn't really like the Espolón; it was too noisy and there were too many people. Instead he would show me the Isla where he lived. It was a continuation of the riverside walk but less popular with the townsfolk as there was a road running alongside it. This didn't matter too much as the traffic there was negligible, just the odd mule or ox cart.

For a while we just walked along in silence. Luis was looking nervous again which made me feel the same. At last I asked him if he knew Anita or any of her friends. He shook his head. "I don't know many people. You see I have been away from Burgos for some time." He hesitated then went on: "I didn't want to tell you this but I suppose you will find out anyway. You see, I have been ill: Tuberculosis. In fact I've only just come out of the sanatorium. I'm cured now, but I was there two years. Two years! Imagine that! It's ruined my studies." I thought to myself, no wonder he looks so pale.

"I shall feel such a fool when I go back to university. Me – twenty-two among all those teenagers."

"A few years don't make any difference. No one will notice."

He looked so depressed that I longed to take his hand, to comfort him, an impulse which I curbed with some difficulty. Then suddenly his mood changed.

"Let's go dancing!" he suggested impulsively.

"Where?"

"The Sala de Fiestas of course. Haven't you been there? You'll like it."

I had heard of the Sala de Fiestas. It was the local nightclub, the only one in Burgos and, according to the Vázquez family, it did not have a very good reputation. However, I didn't care where I went so long as I was with Luis, so I agreed.

The Sala de Fiestas was full of cigarette smoke and bodies swaying hypnotically in the dim light. There were tables round the edge of the dance floor and a small band was playing a cha-cha-cha which seemed to be the most popular dance in Spain. We sat down and Luis ordered gin. I had mine with lemon but he drank his neat and after a few glasses his pale face became quite flushed. I thought: how these Spaniards drink and I am becoming just as bad! What would my parents think? However, alcohol was having a beneficial effect on my companion, who was becoming much more relaxed. We talked about Madrid, a city we both knew and loved and compared notes on the various night spots we had frequented there. He was smiling at me across the table and I felt ecstatically happy, the lustful Vázquez and his gloomy household now quite forgotten. Luis's soft voice was saying: "Let's dance!"

We joined the swaying couples on the dance floor, his arms closed around me, and as we locked together, we were both trembling. I put my cheek against his hot face in a delirium of happiness.

03 80

Unfortunately, Vázquez had now returned from Portugal so my typing lessons had to stop for the moment. I continued to see Luis in the evenings and this made life bearable for my boss was becoming increasingly difficult. Since the bedroom episode, he had been extremely disagreeable, scowling at me morosely while I gave him his lessons. Also, he had not paid me for a month.

"You are going out too much," he said one day. "All this going out in the evenings will have to stop as from next week.

Tomasín will be at school and you must give him his lessons later. In the day time you will teach me and the younger children."

This was a bitter blow but there was nothing I could do about it. At least I would still have Sundays free to see Luis or my other friends. I decided that I had better take advantage of the few remaining free evenings left to me.

Anita telephoned and complained that I had been neglecting her and the others just lately. I apologised and we arranged to meet that same evening. I felt sorry and a bit guilty about not having seen her for so long for she was a very good friend. I would have to offer some explanation. Damn Puck! I could hardly tell her I was hopelessly, helplessly, stupidly, head-over-heels in love.

I met Anita and we walked along the crowded Espolón. I noticed that she was looking particularly pretty that evening and was attracting a lot of compliments. She listened to them with the ear of a connoisseur. If the compliment met with her approval, she would smile, if it did not she would mutter '*sosos*', which, loosely translated, means 'spineless lot'. If, as was often the case, the compliment was of a dubious nature and came from some randy old man, she would treat it with the contempt it deserved and ignore it completely. This was her reaction when, at that moment, a drunken lecher of advancing years sidled up and muttered in her ear: "I could have ten children with you, *Guapa!*"

"Well, you're certainly popular tonight," I remarked. I've never heard so many *piropos*."

"That's one I could do without," she laughed.

There was a shout from a nearby café table and we saw Marisol, Sergio and Felipe. We joined them and sat for a while drinking coffee. Felipe had a copy of '*El Ruedo*' spread out on the table and was poring over it, studying the list of matadors and bulls due to fight in Madrid the following Sunday. "Last fight of the season," he was muttering, "bulls from the best ranches in Spain and the best they can find to fight them are these three lousy matadors. It's unbelievable. What's happened to Dominguín?"

"In South America," said Sergio. "You should know that."

"Do we have to talk about bullfighting?" complained Anita. "It's so boring and I hate it anyway. It's cruel."

Felipe gave a snort of disgust and returned to his magazine and Sergio resumed his favourite occupation – gazing at Marisol. Poor Sergio! Now I knew just how he felt. Whereas before I had merely found the situation amusing, I now felt nothing but the deepest sympathy for him because his plight was so much worse than mine. At least my affections were not altogether unrequited whereas Sergio's case seemed hopeless.

We played a game of cards but I found it difficult to concentrate. I was thinking about Luis and wondering how I could possibly survive, seeing him only once a week. Anita was saying: "Hey! Wake up! What's the matter? You're miles away."

By this time the others had gone home and there were just the two of us left.

"Oh, sorry! No, nothing's the matter."

"Fibber! Of course there is. Do you know what I think? I think you're in love. Don't be so secretive, tell me who it is! We're supposed to be friends."

"Don't be ridiculous!" I laughed, trying to sound convincing. "I'm not in love with anyone."

"You must think me very stupid. Of course you're in love. You have all the symptoms. I'd say you've got it pretty badly too. There's no need to be ashamed of it you know, we're all in love. Sergio is and so am I. I have a *novio* in Oviedo. We write to each other every day, only..." here a small cloud crossed her face momentarily, "he hasn't been writing so often lately and his letters are getting cold. I don't think he loves me any more."

"He's a fool if he doesn't," I said.

"Anyway, we're talking about *you*, not me. So who is it? Is it Felipe?"

"You're crazy!"

"Sergio then? That's no good, he's in love with Marisol and I would have thought that was pretty obvious."

"You're being absurd..."

"Don Federico?" she persisted teasingly. "He's much too old for you and he's already married. Surely it can't be Gonzalo!"

"Alright, alright! Since you're so curious I suppose I'd better tell you. Yes, there is someone but it's no one you know."

Suddenly Anita became serious. Her dark, starry eyes searched my face earnestly.

"You really do think me stupid, don't you? Of course I know who it is. You've been seen out with him enough times. It's Luis Martínez, that consumptive medical student who lives somewhere along the Isla."

"He's not consumptive anymore," I said defensively. Even his illness, horrible as I knew it to be, seemed vaguely romantic, associating it as I did, with geniuses such as Chopin and Keats.

"That's as it maybe," said my friend. "He may be good-looking but he's still not very healthy and he's a terrible introvert. Anyway, you'd better forget him straight away because he already has a *novia*. Everybody knows he's engaged to the institute gardener's daughter."

CHAPTER SIX

CRISIS

The long, hot summer days were over and with them went the carefree Sunday excursions with Anita and the others to the river. No more bathing or catching crayfish to cook on wood fires, no more picnicking, no gathering of juicy, sweet mulberries. September had melted into October and everything was different. With the coming of autumn, the Castilian countryside no longer looked bleak and arid. Everywhere there was colour. Red maples and golden poplars shone in the sun against a backdrop of brilliant blue. Behind the little houses nestling among their brown fields, the distant lavender hills now had a slightly misty appearance. Everything was warm and mellow and I loved it.

My romance with Luis was unfurling and blossoming gently like a flower in the sunshine, watched over and tended by Federico in the role of a benevolent Friar Lawrence. Unwisely, I paid no attention to Anita's warning. Love being deaf as well as blind, I did not believe in the institute gardener's daughter. I thrust her out of my mind. In fact I brain-washed myself into believing that she didn't really exist. Perhaps Anita was playing a mischievous joke on me. Even if this girl were real, I told myself, and there had once been something between her and Luis, she had probably grown tired of waiting for him while he was in the sanatorium and had found someone else. Besides, if he still loved her, why was he with me?

Meanwhile, life in the Vázquez household was becoming increasingly unpleasant. I still had to keep my door locked and now, to make matters worse, I was not getting paid. I could see that Vázquez was putting on the pressure, probably out of spite at being thwarted in his amorous intentions. The atmosphere was terrible. The final blow fell when he announced that as from the following week, my Sundays would no longer be free. I was to teach the family English when they returned from Mass and also in the afternoon.

"But this means that I shall have no free time at all!" I protested.

"Of course you will have free time. You have plenty of time in the afternoons in the week."

"But that's when all my friends are busy. I shall never be able to see them. And another thing – you owe me a lot of money."

"I do *not*," he snarled with a face of thunder and it was obviously futile to argue with him. The situation was becoming intolerable and I toyed with the idea of returning to England. Only my obsession with Luis and my fondness for Burgos and all my friends prevented me from booking my ticket that very day. I rang Anita and told her that I would not be able to meet her on the Sunday as had been arranged and explained why. I felt near to weeping and Anita was stunned.

"You must leave," she said, "you can't stay there under those conditions."

"I can't leave. I've grown so fond of Burgos. I can't go home now. Perhaps Don Tomás will relent."

The following Sunday morning I went to look for Federico to tell him the news but he was not in his academy, nor was he in the Bar Paloma. Since I did not have time to search all the bars in Burgos I started to walk home. Suddenly I heard someone calling me and turning, I saw Raúl, the doctor in whose company I had spent that last evening in Santander.

"Hello!" he said, "How are you getting on? Do you like it here in Burgos?"

"Yes, I like Burgos, but I am not happy in Vázquez's house."

I told him all my grievances: how he didn't pay me, how he was determined that I should have no free time. "Do you know, – I haven't told anybody this – but Don Tomás even tries to get into my room at night. I have to lock my door. It's awful!"

Raúl nodded gravely. He clearly was not very surprised.

"Whatever happens," he advised, "keep that a secret. If people were to get to know it they would think you were having an affair with him. It would be *your* reputation, not Tomás's that would suffer."

I thought: how unfair! Maybe I had better leave this backward country.

Cʒ ᙠ

That evening I joined Luis and his brothers in a room above a bar. The older brothers had been out shooting that morning and we were all going to have a feast of roast hare and wine. The brothers were very different from Luis, both in character and appearance. They were sturdy lads, convivial and extrovert almost to the point of being over-bearing. The wine flowed freely and we all became very merry, singing and exchanging jokes. It helped me to forget, for the moment, the unpleasant task which lay ahead: that of telling Luis I would be returning to England shortly. Earlier, at lunch time, I had finally made up my mind that I would go home, bitterly as I regretted having to do so, for it seemed I had no choice.

Luis, after several glasses of wine, had become lively and vociferous. It was hard to believe, looking at him now, that he was the same shy, diffident young man who had walked into Federico's academy a few weeks ago. With one arm round my neck and the other holding his glass aloft, he cried: "I give you a toast! To the Spanish Republic! *Viva La Republica Española!*"

I was amazed and startled. Where was all the caution he had shown when telling me about his father?

His brothers, who had stronger heads, leapt to their feet instantly and rushed over to suppress this indiscreet outburst of political fervour.

"You idiot!" snapped Ignacio, a note of panic in his voice. "Do you want us all arrested? Have you been out of circulation so long you've forgotten what it's like in the real world? You'd better get out of here before we all end up in the political prison."

"What sort of life is this?" demanded Luis angrily, getting to

57

his feet and swaying slightly, his green eyes ablaze. "If I had the chance I *would* get out of here. I would go anywhere, *anywhere* rather than stay here."

Ignacio walked over to me and bent to whisper in my ear. "He's had too much to drink. He's always like this when he's had too many. One day this will happen in a public place, someone will hear and that will be the end of him. For God's sake get him out into the fresh air and make him sober up!"

"Come on Luis," I said, gently taking him by the arm, "let's go for a walk."

A chilly breeze sent the fallen leaves scurrying along the pavement. Luis shivered and pulled up his collar, his face deathly pale under the dim street lights. We stopped while he lit a cigarette then stood leaning against the parapet gazing down at the river below, watching the shimmering reflections of lights dancing on the dark water.

"What sort of country is this where a man can't speak his mind without fear of being arrested?" he brooded. "What must you think of us?"

"Let's forget it," I suggested.

"Forget it? Forget it? How can one forget it? You don't know how lucky you are to live in a free country."

"Oh yes I do. Since living here I really appreciate what we have back home."

"They rule our lives." His voice was bitter. "And they killed my father. I can't forget that. They *murdered* my father and I want to shout that from the rooftops."

I looked at him and what I saw in his face frightened me. It was hatred: pure, unashamed, terrifyingly intense hatred and I didn't like it.

"Luis, Let's forget politics for a minute. I have something important to tell you. You see, this may be the last time we see each other for a long time because I've decided to go home, back to England."

He stared at me in astonishment and removed the cigarette from his mouth. "You're not serious?"

"I am."

"Back to your *free* country? Has it got you down already, living here? *Ay! Dios!*" He passed his hand across his face.

"No! No! It has nothing to do with politics. Of course I don't want to go home yet but I have no alternative. You know how impossible life is becoming at that house and now Vázquez has stopped paying me and he's not going to allow me any free time. That's the last straw. I shall have to leave."

Luis seized my hand. "But you can't go. You don't mean it. Please listen to me! I love you. You know that, don't you? I have loved you since that first day when I saw you at Don Federico's academy. Remember that silly frog of Paco's? But I didn't think I had a chance. I thought you would have a boyfriend in England."

He clasped me to him and I buried my head in his shoulder not wanting him to see my tears. Perhaps it was the effect of the wine but I had never known him to talk so long without stopping.

"You're the best thing that's ever happened to me," he continued breathlessly, "you have restored all my self confidence: all the confidence I lost while I was in the sanatorium and I want you to be with me all the time. *Dios mío!* How I want you!"

"I can't bear the thought of leaving you, Luis, but what choice do I have? I can't work for nothing. I'm not his slave."

"Listen!" His voice was suddenly calmer. "There is a way out of this. You don't have to stay in that house. You could easily make a living teaching English. Everybody wants to learn English since the Americans set up their bases in Spain. There are cheap guest houses in Burgos. Why stay with Vázquez?"

This was an idea that had not occurred to me. It took a while to sink in but gradually my misery subsided as I realised that Luis really had shown me an escape route. However, I still had lingering doubts.

"Do you really think I could find enough pupils for me to live independently here in Burgos?"

"Why not? I'm sure of it; and later, when I go back to Madrid, I want you to be there with me. There are masses of people in Madrid who want to learn English and we could be so happy there together!"

This all sounded easy and irresistibly tempting. I imagined

myself strolling with Luis by the lake in Madrid's Retiro Park, window-gazing along the smart Gran Vía or enjoying a drink at the romantic Cuevas de Luis Candelas. Together we would admire the paintings in the Prado Gallery and go dancing at the Casa del Segoviano. It was my idea of heaven and you don't turn your back on heaven.

"I'll do it," I said with determination, straightening myself and drying my eyes. "Tomorrow I shall give in my notice to Vázquez, but I'm staying in Spain whatever happens."

"You promise that?"

"Yes. But you must promise me that there will be no more of this dangerous talk about the Republic. I want you with me in one piece and I want you to be happy."

He smiled. "There's only one thing that can make me happy and that's if you stay here and be my *novia*."

My joy knew no bounds now that I could be sure of Luis's feelings towards me. The sinister spectre of the institute gardener's daughter had at last been exorcised and he was mine. My head was in the clouds as we walked back along the Espolón and I could never remember feeling so happy.

On that chilly, autumnal night the Espolón was very different from the way it had been a month ago. Gone were the strolling crowds. It was windswept and deserted except for a few people hurrying home. The café owners were stacking away their tables and chairs and the pavements looked bare and forlorn. Nevertheless, that evening I viewed everything through a warm, rosy glow. Everything and everyone seemed wonderful.

Alas, this state of euphoria was short-lived and I was quickly brought down to earth again on arriving back at the Vázquez house. As soon as I entered I could sense that something was wrong. Even Rosa was not her usual calm self. She was setting the table in the dining room arranging then re-arranging the cutlery in a flustered way. When she saw me she apologised that dinner would be late. "There's been a bit of trouble with the cook," she said.

"Why, what's happened?"

"Oh… nothing. It's just that the cook is rather upset, that's all."

Her manner was nervous and evasive so I decided to see for myself. In the kitchen I found the cook frying potatoes. Her face was red and swollen and she looked generally ruffled.

"What's the matter Mercedes?"

She passed her sleeve across her face and sniffed. "I'm leaving," she announced in a strangled voice. "I'm giving in my notice."

"Tell me what's happened!"

Silently she unbuttoned the back of her dress and pulled it down to reveal her bare shoulder and back which were covered with angry red marks. I stared at them in horror.

"You've been beaten!" I gasped. "The Mistress?"

The cook nodded. "I'm leaving," she repeated buttoning up her dress. "I won't be treated like this. It's too much."

"I don't blame you! And I'll tell you another thing. You're not the only one who will be leaving this house."

I turned and walked out of the kitchen and at that moment the telephone rang.

"It's for you señorita," said Rosa.

"Listen!" Anita's voice sounded excited. "Listen! I've been thinking about what you said and I have an idea. You could give English classes here in Burgos and earn a lot of money. I know several people who would be interested. Aunt Domi says you can come and live with us if you like. There's not a lot of room here but we can squeeze you in. Please say you will!"

I could hardly believe my good fortune. There was now nothing to prevent me leaving Vázquez and I went to my room and started to pack determined to do so the very next day.

Cß ᘒ

The following morning dawned fine and sunny. The cold wind had dropped and it was a beautiful, golden day. I had promised Anita that I would arrive on her doorstep complete with my suitcase some time that afternoon. As I did not have to look for accommodation and Vázquez had not paid me for a long time, I could see no reason why I shouldn't leave immediately without giving notice.

When Rosa came into my room to dust, she stared in amazement at my packed case and empty cupboards.

"Surely you are not going today? What will you do? Where will you go, señorita?" She seemed genuinely concerned.

I laughed. "Don't you worry about me Rosa! I'll be alright. Yes, I've every intention of leaving today. After what I saw last night I don't want to stay here another minute."

Rosa sighed and a strange look came over her face as though she were wishing she too had the freedom to leave. I wondered why she did not. What mystery was this girl hiding? Could it be that Vázquez had forced his attentions on her too, with success, and was now subjecting her to blackmail? I remembered what Raúl had said. A bad reference implying that her morals were loose would be enough to guarantee she would never find employment elsewhere.

Lunchtime arrived. I decided to have a quick meal with the children and then face Vázquez before he left for the clinic. He and Doña Constanza were having their lunch as usual at the end of the vast table in the dining room. They did not even look up when I entered the room but continued stuffing themselves in silence. I summoned up all my courage, took a deep breath and began.

"Don Tomás, I'm sorry I have to disturb you in the middle of a meal but I have something important to say to you and it cannot wait."

"We are eating," muttered Vázquez with his mouth full. "Wait till we have finished!"

"There's no time. You will be leaving the house after lunch and so will I. My bags are packed and there's nothing to keep me here any longer."

"What do you mean?" spluttered Vázquez, nearly spilling his wine. "What are you talking about? Get out and leave us in peace!"

"No! You will hear me out!" I could feel my face flushing with anger. "You expect me to work for you for nothing with no free time to see my friends but that is not what we agreed when I first came here. You have gone back on your word and you owe me a lot of money. Since I have been here I have not been happy for a number of reasons of which you, Don Tomás, are only too aware."

"Get out!" shouted Vázquez wiping his mouth on his napkin. "I don't know what you are talking about. We are having a meal."

I looked at Doña Constanza who had been sitting there opening and closing her red mouth like a fish. I decided to take pity on her. I could not tell her what was in my mind!

"Don Tomás, whether you listen to me or not makes no difference. The fact is that my bags are in the hall and I am leaving right now, but before I do so, I would ask you to settle the amount you owe me, my salary for the past two months."

I handed him a piece of paper on which I had written out an account for my services. He tore it up angrily throwing the pieces on the floor. "I owe you nothing!" he yelled, his face scarlet with rage. "Do you hear me? I owe you *nothing – now get out of this room!*"

I could see that Vázquez did not think I was serious. He obviously assumed I was bluffing for as I left the room, he picked up his fork and resumed eating as though nothing had happened.

I went into the living room to say goodbye to Tomasín. He was home from school with a cold and was feeling sorry for himself.

"Goodbye," I said. "I expect Don Federico will be teaching you English as well as Latin from now on. Poor Federico! Anyway, I'm leaving so goodbye. I hope your cold will soon be better."

"Going somewhere?" he croaked, clearing his throat and spitting enthusiastically on the carpet.

"Yes, I am and I can't get there quick enough. Incidentally, that's disgusting. Poor Rosa will have to clear up that mess."

"So what? That's her job isn't it? That's what she's paid for. Got to give her something to do."

"Pig!"

I turned to go, but he leapt to his feet and ran after me.

"Hey, you're not *really* going, are you?"

"Watch me!"

I marched into the hall, where I had left my things. Through the half-open dining room door I could see that Vázquez and Doña Constanza were still eating. The servants were all standing in the hall eager to see whether I would be true to my word. I picked up my case and smiled at them.

"Goodbye Rosa, Josefina, Mercedes. I wish you luck because here you're going to need it!"

I walked out of the flat, making as dignified an exit as I could with my arms full of bags and descended the stairs. At the bottom I looked up and saw three astonished heads leaning over the banisters. I put down one of my cases and gave them a last wave but they were too dumbfounded to respond.

Out in the sunshine I felt like a released prisoner. My bags were heavy but my heart was light as I walked down the street and through the market on my way to Anita's house. I pushed through the throng, steering a course between the many stalls laden with scarlet pimientos, heavy bunches of bananas, clusters of grapes and crates of water melons. A man roasting chestnuts and another selling *churros* competed with each other, shouting out their wares in loud voices. I paused for a moment, putting my luggage down to rest my arms and admire the display of earthenware pots and plates which lay spread out on the pavement. Their owner was sitting propped up against a wall, his head flopped forward on his chest, hat pulled down over his eyes, oblivious to the noisy world around him. There was an empty *porrón* at his elbow and I marvelled at the trusting nature which allowed him to indulge in drunken slumbers while his wares were on display to the public in such a vulnerable way.

"Señorita!" A voice called behind me and I started, like a hunted animal, fearful that someone from the Vázquez household had been sent to pursue me and was about to drag me kicking and screaming back to the dreadful place. I turned quickly, nearly tripping over some chickens which sat basking at my feet. "Señorita, where are you going with all those things? What has happened?"

To my immense relief, I saw that it was the vegetable seller with whom I was on good terms having bought water melons from her regularly for Mercedes. She came out from behind her stall and peered at me anxiously.

"It's alright," I said, "I've left the place where I was working but everything's fine…"

"*Madre mía!* But where will you go? You are very welcome to stay in my house if you wish. There's only my son and myself. We could easily find room for one more."

I was moved by this spontaneous gesture of hospitality: such readiness to accept a virtual stranger into her home. I explained that I was going to friends and thanked her warmly for her offer. But she was still full of motherly concern for my welfare.

"You cannot carry all those heavy things so far. It's a long way, on the edge of town. Come! Let my son take them for you."

"Oh no," I protested, "I couldn't let him do that. I can manage – honestly!"

"Nonsense, it will be no trouble to him. Pepe! Pepe!"

Her son, a brown, smiling lad stepped forward and picked up my bags. The warmth and kindness of these people, whom I hardly knew, seemed to compensate for everything I had experienced at the Vázquez house.

So I set off once more accompanied now by Pepe. His presence was surprisingly reassuring as I still had the uneasy feeling that I might be followed. He chatted to me as we walked along past the convent and the bullring and eventually up the rough, stony road that led to Anita's house. How cosy and welcoming it looked with its pink tiles and yellow shutters bathed in the mellow autumnal sunshine! I saw Aunt Domi standing in the doorway, looking out for me and I felt as joyful as if I were returning to my own home.

CHAPTER SEVEN

PUPILS AND TOURISTS

The advertisement in the 'Diario de Burgos' read: *English girl gives private lessons in English at all levels in the comfort and privacy of your own home.*

The day after it appeared the telephone in Anita's house never stopped ringing. It seemed the whole of Burgos was eager to learn English and I spent a busy few days visiting prospective pupils and arranging a timetable of classes. Although my fees were as modest as I could make them, with reduced rates for groups, I was soon aware that, with such a large number of pupils, I was going to make a tidy sum. My timetable would be tight and I would be working hard, six days a week. But I was elated at the prospect of being totally independent financially and in a position to help Anita's family who had provided me with a roof over my head. I also had a secret plan to take Anita with me on a trip to the south of Spain after Christmas.

At first it worried me that I might be taking business from Don Federico but then I remembered him saying he had more pupils wanting to learn English than he could cope with and had had to turn some of them away. Besides, I could now resume my typing lessons and help him with his advanced students as before. Soon after I had left Vázquez I bumped into Federico so I was able to recount to him the momentous events of the last few days. He approved of everything I had done and immediately offered me the use of his academy for teaching groups three afternoons a week. Could anyone ask for better friends?

My new pupils included four junior doctors from the local hospital, a businessman, the young daughter of an affluent family, several middle-aged single ladies, and a few students. Strangest of all – and much to my surprise – I was summoned by the *Capitán General* to teach his daughters. He was the Regional Military Governor, a formidable and much-feared man of great importance whose rank and achievements, so I was told, placed him high in Franco's hierarchy.

It was therefore with some trepidation that I climbed the steps of his palatial residence, this being the military headquarters for the region known as the *Capitanía*. On either side of the massive entrance several armed guards stood staring ahead, their weapons glinting in the sun. They reminded me of the frightening stories I had heard of dissidents who had been arrested, taken to this place and never seen again.

When I reached the top of the steps they barred my way with their rifles and demanded to know my business. I was told to wait while enquiries were made and, after a few tense moments, I was ushered in. Complete with military escort, I mounted yet more flights of steps, arriving eventually at the sumptuous apartments of the Great Man.

The room was furnished with deep-pile oriental rugs and heavy antique furniture. There were fewer potted plants than in Vázquez's house, but many more canaries. They seemed to be everywhere, trilling, chirping and hopping about in their numerous cages so that one had the impression of being in some strange aviary. A tabby cat of gigantic size was sitting on the arm of one of the chairs, staring at me suspiciously with unblinking eyes. Another rushed past my legs as I crossed the room.

Seated at a table, surrounded by canaries, were the two daughters of the Captain General. They were of uncertain age and inclined to plumpness. Their lips and nails were painted a deep red and their hair was bleached an unlikely shade of blonde which contrasted oddly with their olive skins and dark eyes. Smiling, they rose to greet me.

"*Buenos días,*" one of them said. "Please sit down. We are so looking forward to learning English."

We came to an arrangement about times and fees and, as we were chatting, I felt something furry against my legs. Looking down I observed yet another cat. It slunk out from under the table and I bent to stroke it. This was a mistake, for it turned and hissed at me, bristling with indignation. Having made clear its disapproval, it leapt onto a nearby cupboard from where it was able to study the birds at close quarters. The poor creatures stopped singing and hopped about nervously under its scrutiny.

"I see you have a lot of cats," I observed.

"Yes," said the younger daughter. She reached down to gather up a passing black Persian and set it on her lap where it crouched grudgingly, ears back, staring angrily into space. "Do you like them? This one is called Tín-tín, aren't you darling?"

My sympathy was with the canaries living as they obviously did in constant fear of these ill-intentioned felines.

"Do they ever catch the canaries?" I ventured to ask.

The older daughter smiled. "Sometimes," she said, "sometimes one of the servants leaves a door open and one of them escapes from its cage and then…" she shrugged her shoulders. "Well, what do you expect?"

It crossed my mind that here was some kind of sinister symbolism.

"They're really father's pets," she added. "You see, Papá is very fond of cats."

03 80

Out in the street once more, I looked at my watch and decided I had time to buy some stamps before going back to Anita's for lunch. I had written a letter to my family and was anxious to get it posted so I walked across to the little tobacconist on the corner of the square where I usually bought stamps.

Among the people waiting to be served I noticed a couple who stood out from the rest. They were tall and fair with pale, untanned skin and brightly coloured clothes which marked them as aliens among the Spanish customers. As soon as they started trying to explain their requirements to the assistant I knew them to be my fellow-countrymen. They were having some difficulty in making themselves understood so I stepped forward.

"Can I help?" I asked in English. "Tell me what you want and

I'll get it for you."

An expression of relief crossed the young man's face. "Oh thanks! We don't seem to be getting very far. We just need to know how much the postage is to England."

Their letters safely posted, I was invited to join them for a coffee at a nearby café. We chatted and they told me they were Audrey and Peter from Birmingham and they were taking a late holiday. They had decided to break their journey to Madrid and had booked into the Hotel Ávila. "Rather a grotty sort of place," observed Peter, "but cheap. I suppose it will be OK."

As I had no other pupils to interview that day, I offered to show them the sights of Burgos so we arranged to meet later that afternoon.

On my way back to Anita's house, I suddenly saw Paco emerging from a bar closely followed by Luis. I felt my heart racing as it always did whenever I set eyes on him for the spell was as powerful as ever.

"There she is!" laughed Paco, "That independent English *miss!* We've heard all about it you know – from Federico. Fancy walking out on Vázquez like that! The old man's livid; been looking for you all over the place."

Luis was smiling. "Yes, It's caused quite a sensation. The talk of the town!" he affirmed.

I looked at him and longed to rush into his arms not having seen him for a week which seemed more like a year. We stood gazing at each other while Paco rambled on.

"I bet you've found dozens of pupils already. I should think anyone would want to learn English from a girl like you. I know several friends who might be interested. I was just saying to Luis – everyone wants to learn English since the Yanks set up their bases here…"

Paco talked and talked but we were not really listening. When at last there was a pause in the flow I said: "Now that I'm my own boss, I shall be taking up my typing lessons again with Federico, starting next week."

Luis caught my hand. "Then we shall see each other a lot more, *Cariño,* because I shall be there too."

I sighed happily at this idyllic prospect and Paco groaned.

"Oh, give it a rest you two! I've never seen such a crazy pair. I wonder what will happen when…"

He stopped suddenly, thinking better of whatever it was he was going to say. Luis threw him a withering glance and he continued in some confusion. "I mean … I wonder what you will do without her, Luis, when you go back to university…"

"Sorry," I interrupted, "I must go. Look at the time! I'm late as it is."

"Oh, this British obsession with time!" laughed Paco.

I hurried back to Aunt Domi's lunch, wondering uneasily what Paco was going to say. He obviously knew something I didn't about Luis; something concerning us which Luis didn't want me to know. This worrying thought hovered around in my head despite all efforts to banish it.

ഓ ൠ

"What time do the banks re-open?" asked Peter as we left the cathedral.

I laughed. "You won't find them open again today. It's Saturday. You'll have to wait till Monday morning."

He looked at me in horror. "Hell! We've no money to pay the hotel, only enough pesetas to buy petrol and we must be in Madrid by tomorrow evening. What are we going to do?"

We hurried to the local tourist office where we were told that only first class hotels were authorised to change travellers' cheques and the Hotel Ávila was definitely *not* first class. "However," suggested the clerk, "you could go along to the Hotel España and ask if they would change some money for you as a favour."

"Oh, please come with us and explain!" pleaded Audrey who was near to tears. "We don't speak a word of Spanish and no one understands us. It's awful."

At the Hotel España the receptionist was decidedly cool. No, he was sorry, but it was quite impossible. They could only change cheques for their own clients and not, he affirmed with a sniff of contempt, for those of the Hotel Ávila.

Dejectedly we walked away from the smart Hotel España, gleaming white and smug on the corner of the Espolón, and made our way down a shabby back street to find the Hotel Ávila, a tatty place which looked as though it had never heard of travellers' cheques. I was just examining the meagre contents of my purse to see what money I could lend them when Peter was suddenly struck with a brilliant idea.

"Look! We've any amount of French francs. Suppose we were to book a room here for our return journey, leave the equivalent of this amount in francs as security and pay everything in pesetas on our return?"

I said: "That makes sense – if the hotel agrees. Do they speak English?"

They both laughed. "You must be joking! Does *anyone* speak English here?"

"Not yet," I grinned, "but I plan to change all that!"

We walked into the dark, chilly hall and asked for the manager. He emerged, smiling, from his inner sanctum, a tall, good-looking and surprisingly young man with a roving eye. He looked me up and down as I explained my friends' predicament.

"Why yes, of course, señorita, that will be quite in order. I'll make out a receipt for the francs and they can book a room here for their return. No problem. By the way, did anyone tell you that you have nice eyes?"

The problem resolved, Audrey and Peter retired to their room for a siesta but not before making me promise to meet them again that evening for a drink in the Espolón.

⋐ ⋑

As usual, the kitchen at Anita's house was packed with people. A neighbour, Miguel, had come round for a chat together with his wife, Mari and two little girls, Patricia and Isabelita. Cousin Bea had also arrived, out of the blue, with her husband, Jaime, and small daughter, Marta. They were all gathered together for *merienda*, a snack taken in the early evening to bridge the long gap between lunch at two and supper at around eleven. As I squeezed my way into the warm, smoky little room I saw that Miguel was holding a baguette, poised above the table. He was discussing some political matter with Aunt Domi and thumping the bread on the table with thuds to add emphasis to the points he was making. Aunt Domi responded in shrill tones as she stood by her sizzling frying pan, preparing the evening meal. The children sat on a bench by the table, their ceaseless chatter temporarily silenced as they gave their attention to great hunks of bread filled with slabs of cooking chocolate. Cousin Bea, apparently, had toothache and was not prepared to suffer in silence. With one hand clutching her painful jaw and the other spread across her ample bosom, she sat rocking backwards and forwards sighing and moaning loudly: *"Ay! Ay! Ay!"*

Everyone greeted me enthusiastically, eager to know what I had been doing and how many pupils I had collected that day. I was wedged into a corner of the table where Aunt Domi presented me with a large cup of coffee. "Get that inside you!" she ordered, pointing to the cup with her fork. "And some bread. It's time you fattened up. You foreign girls are as skinny as rakes. Look at the girl! No flesh on her anywhere."

"Never mind that!" interrupted Mari. "Let's hear about her pupils! Where have you been today?"

"Well," I said, trying to sound casual, "as from next week, I shall be teaching the two daughters of the Captain General."

"You're joking!" said Miguel. I shook my head, enjoying myself.

"You've been *there*?" gasped Mari.

"To the Capitanía?" cried Bea in astonishment, her toothache temporarily forgotten. "Did you see him? Did you see the Captain General? What's he like?"

"I didn't see the Captain General," I explained when I could get a word in edgeways, "but I know one thing about him. He likes cats."

"But you're surely not going to teach those people?" protested Mari.

"Why not? Of course I shall teach them, the same as anyone else. I'm not fussy."

"Make sure you charge them plenty," grunted Domi, refilling my cup.

"I charge everyone the same," I retorted virtuously. "I intend to conduct my business in a thoroughly British way. As for the daughters, they're really quite nice."

At that moment Anita burst into the room looking flushed and out-of-breath. "It's Don Tomás!" she gasped rushing over to me. "He's discovered you're with us and he's absolutely furious – says we've 'captured' you. He's given us eight days to throw you out and after that he'll sack me if you're still in the house."

This was terrible news. It really shook me and I felt extremely guilty at having brought trouble to a family who had shown me so much kindness. I knew what I had to do and I got up from the table.

"I'll pack at once. You're not losing your job because of me. I can find a *pensión*."

Anita laughed and pulled me down onto my chair. "Don't be silly! Just listen to me! I've given in my notice. I've quit the job. I was going to leave anyway – before you arrived – because I've had enough of his groping hands in the dark room when we're looking at X-rays. Honestly! It's like wrestling with an octopus in there. All the nurses complain about it."

"Yes," I nodded. "I know what you mean."

"Disgusting!" snorted Aunt Domi, jabbing angrily at the contents of her frying pan. "The man's a lecher and everyone knows it, including his wife."

"You're better off working somewhere else," added Miguel, "no young girl's safe with him around."

"And in the meantime," I said, "none of you will be out of pocket because I'm going to earn a lot of money. You'll have more than enough house-keeping from me, Auntie Domi, and quite a few little luxuries besides."

"Bless you, child," muttered Domi wiping her eyes with the corner of her apron. "You're one of us now: one of the family and this is your home for as long as you need it."

⋯

The waiter at the café in the Espolón knew me and beamed benevolently as I sat down with Audrey and Peter and ordered our drinks. I was busy telling my new friends all about my adventures in Burgos and he was obviously amused and intrigued to hear me speaking my native tongue.

"I can't imagine why you want to spend so long in this odd place," remarked Audrey. "I mean, it's really rather a strange life for an English girl and it doesn't sound at all safe. Listen! I have an idea. Why don't you come home with us? We could pick you up on our way back and it would save you the return fare."

"Good idea!" agreed Peter. "You do that."

"It's really kind of you to offer but I can't leave Burgos yet. My life is here at the moment and I've grown quite fond of this funny old town. I'm living with a lovely family now and I've lots of pupils lined up. Besides, there's another reason. I've fallen in love with a Spanish student."

Audrey's eyes widened in amazement. "You've *what?*"

I nodded. "It's true and I can't do a thing about it. I'm head over heels. It's never happened to me before and it's a pretty awesome experience! There's no way I could leave him now."

Audrey sighed. "I expect you'll get over it. How old are you? Nineteen? You've got plenty of time. One day you'll be sensible and find a nice, steady Englishman and you'll marry him and settle down."

I smiled at this most unlikely scenario and shook my head. What a ludicrous prediction!

"We are quite worried about you though," said Peter, "leaving you in this extraordinary place."

"But I like it! How can I convince you? You don't need to worry. I'm among friends."

I was amused at their concern. It was as though they had discovered me, vulnerable and defenceless in the heart of the African bush but I could understand their point of view. Tourism was only just beginning to build up in Spain and this was an unusual place to visit – let alone live in! It was considered primitive, like a Third World country, ruled by a ruthless dictatorship whose victory in the Civil War had been assisted by

Nazi Germany. I remembered the difficulty I'd had in persuading my father to endorse my passport application form when I first visited Spain.

"Well, be careful, anyway," warned Peter. "This place is seething with political tension and there could be an insurgency at any time."

I had to agree. I knew there were secret police everywhere watching and listening.

"Not much fun," observed Peter wryly. Audrey looked around her and said she thought it was time they were getting back to the hotel. "We have a long journey ahead of us and we have to be up early," she said, pulling on her cardigan. "Come on Peter!"

Two civil guards had just entered the café and were deep in conversation with the barman. Remembering Don Tomás's quest for me, I decided it was time I too made a move.

CHAPTER EIGHT

GATHERING CLOUDS AND A VILLAGE WEDDING

"Hay agua! Hay agua!" shrieked Aunt Domi. This was the clarion call for everyone to rush into the kitchen and grab wine bottles, jugs, mugs, pots and anything else we could lay hands on and race with them to the tiny lavatory where the wash basin tap provided our only source of water. Since we never knew when and for how long the water would be available, it was essential to fill as many containers as possible as fast as possible. It was quite likely that the supply we were collecting now would have to last us for twenty-four hours or more. For most of the summer and autumn, when the tap was turned on, the only result would be a strangled gurgling sound, sometimes, but not always, accompanied by a few rusty drips. So the joyful sight of unlimited water gushing from it would automatically send us into that frenzied scramble.

On this particular day, our task was considerably hampered by the presence of two cockerels which seemed to have taken up residence in the lavatory. Every time someone opened the door to reach for the tap, the birds would make frantic attempts to escape. Twice their efforts were successful and it took Cousin Bea, who had brought the birds, ten minutes of chasing them up and down the stairs and around the house before she eventually managed to recapture them amid much indignant clucking, squawking and the panic-stricken beating of wings.

"Hurry up all of you!" she gasped, clutching the protesting birds, her hair dishevelled, her bosom heaving from the recent exertion. "You're upsetting my birds. Get a move on with those bottles!"

Cousin Bea had been given the cockerels by a friend and it was her intention to make a meal of them as soon as she considered them sufficiently well-fattened. This process consisted of keeping them in a confined space while supplying them with abundant food, hence their occupation of the lavatory. In the meantime, the entire running of the house revolved around their welfare, their comforts taking precedence over those of the rest of us. Unfortunately, they were of an aggressive nature and, from time to time, terrible scuffles would break out and the noise of hostile squawking and fluttering feathers would send Cousin Bea hurtling towards their den where her screams of alarm, as she attempted to separate them, would join the general pandemonium.

I did not look forward to the various visits which, of necessity, I had to make to the place where-in these ill-tempered creatures lurked. That morning, clutching my allotted bottle of water for washing, I paused outside the door, listening nervously before attempting to enter. However, all I could hear was the innocuous sound of their claws scratching in the straw so I opened the door a chink and peered in. Immediately, two heads, armed with vicious-looking beaks thrust themselves through the crack. I pushed them back with my foot and entered hurriedly, closing the door after me in the nick of time as one of them was about to hurl itself into the outside world. Pouring my water into the wash basin, I kept a wary eye on them as they circled menacingly round my legs grumbling to themselves and observing me sideways with their beady eyes.

Washing was never an easy business in that confined space but now it was a thousand times more difficult. Care had to be taken to avoid treading on soiled straw or knocking over their water or food trough. This time I was lucky for I managed to avoid all of these hazards and, better still, the two antagonists seemed to have declared a temporary truce. This was a relief as I was used to seeing them confronting each other on tiptoe, feathers ruffled, spurs at the ready, poised to launch themselves into their next confrontation. While cleaning my teeth I heard the flapping of wings behind me as one of them flew clumsily up onto the cistern. There it stood, head thrust forward, deafening me with its crowing.

This was something we had all learned to live with and alarm clocks were no longer necessary. Every morning, at crack of dawn, we were rudely roused from our slumbers as they vied with each other, making further sleep impossible. They had incredibly loud voices and it seemed the whole house shook to their joyful heralding of a new day. At last, even Cousin Bea grew tired of the many inconveniences – especially the lack of sleep – and so, thankfully, the cockerels were eventually moved to the back yard.

ଓଃ ଔଓ

It was just as well that I had got into the habit of waking early as I was now very busy and had a lot of classes to fit into the day. They were going well. It was a relief to teach people who really wanted to learn and my pupils were becoming my friends. One of them was Señorita Alvárez, a middle-aged unmarried lady of enormous charm and character. Among her many hobbies was the study of the British, their language and quaint customs and on this subject she considered herself something of an authority. Indeed, Señorita Alvárez never ceased to amaze me with her knowledge.

One day, towards the end of the lesson, she set down her book and smiled at me sweetly.

"No more English for today. It's time for refreshments and I have a little surprise for you."

She patted me on the shoulder and left the room to return shortly bearing a tray with a jug, some cups and a plate of something sticky. She set the tray down carefully on the table, throwing me little sideways glances as she did so and then set out the cups, saucers and plates with meticulous care. Next, she picked up the jug and paused for a moment to smile again before pouring its thick, black contents into the cups. Handing me one, she leaned back in her chair to watch my reaction.

"What do you think of that?" she asked.

I took a tentative sip of the strange beverage. It had a very strong, odd flavour: sour, sweet and bitter at the same time and yet there was something vaguely familiar about it.

"English tea!" she announced triumphantly. "In your honour;

I know how you English just love your tea." She was obviously very pleased with her brew.

"How kind of you!" I said.

"And how about *this*?" She leaned forward to pick up the plate of sticky brown confectionery. "Doesn't that make you feel at home?"

"Er – yes," I replied hesitantly, wondering what it was.

"Plum cake. Just for you. You see I know how you English *always* have plum cake with your tea."

"Lovely! You're spoiling me!"

"I knew it would make you happy. I know all your little habits. I think I understand the British having read so many books about your country. I want you to feel quite at home when you come here, my dear. You must get very homesick being so far from your native land. But whenever you feel sad, just come here and I'll make you a cup of tea."

"That's very nice of you, Señorita Alvárez, but at present I don't feel homesick at all."

"How you must miss your family!" she continued, ignoring my last remark. "And your mother must worry about you a great deal. But you can tell her that in me you have a friend to whom you can always turn in times of need."

I walked over to the window. The grey November afternoon was cold and windy and a chilly drizzle pattered against the panes.

"Now this makes me think of home. This is typical English weather," I remarked.

Señorita Alvárez shook her head firmly. "No, not typical. To be typical there must be fog. Am I not right? In England there is always fog."

"Well, not always," I began but my pupil was not listening.

"Yes, always fog. I have seen it in all the films about England. Always there is a policeman with one of those strange, tall hats walking through the swirling mists. I think it must be rather a sad place, always to be surrounded by fog and damp. But there must be compensations," she added brightly, "yes, I am sure there are many compensations."

I could see that she had formed her own mental picture of

England and it would be pointless – even unkind – to disillusion her. I finished my cup of strange tea and the even stranger plum cake and, with renewed thanks for her hospitality, gathered up my books and departed. As I stepped out onto the wet pavement, I was immediately enveloped in a cold sheet of rain that had no difficulty in penetrating my flimsy jacket. I hurried along the semi-deserted streets, shoes squelching in the puddles, hair clinging to my face and water trickling down my neck. Under my jacket I cradled my precious text books hoping, at least, to keep *them* reasonably dry. On the other side of the street I noticed a sandwich man holding an umbrella and bearing a placard appropriately announcing the film that was to be shown the following Sunday at the local cinema: *'Cantando Bajo La Lluvia'* ('Singing in the Rain').

As it happened, I didn't feel at all like singing. I just wanted to get back to the warm comfort of Anita's kitchen as soon as possible. Up to now I hadn't thought about the coming winter. Life in Spain had seemed like one endless summer's day and yet I had been warned that winter in Burgos was both long and harsh. The icy winds from the sierra could cut through you like a knife and there would be plenty of snow. After all, we were at 4,000 feet.

On reflection, I remembered that there had already been hints of the weather to come, like the cold wind that had swept along the Espolón on the evening before I left Vázquez: that evening with Luis. But what had happened to Luis now? Just lately he seemed different: even more remote and withdrawn and preoccupied, as though wrestling with some inner conflict. Even when he kissed me it was with a strange urgency as though each kiss might be the last. Could it be, I wondered with a sting of panic, that the warm summer of this, my first love, was about to fade away into a cruel winter? I felt a sudden shiver down my spine that had nothing to do with the rain.

☙ ❧

The old bus bumped its way across the village square and, with a final shudder of relief, came to a lurching halt. Anita and I, dressed in our best, stepped down gingerly in our stiletto heels which sank instantly into a quagmire of mud. The rain of yesterday had fortunately drifted away, but it had left its mark.

A bevy of girls, who had been waiting for us, ran across the square. They greeted us warmly, chattering and giggling with excitement.

"These are the bride's sisters," explained Anita. "Come on! We must hurry. The bride is waiting to be dressed."

I had not known that we were to attend a wedding until the previous evening when Anita had surprised me with the news while helping to peel off my sodden clothes. I was still not clear as to how we had come to be invited but it appeared that the miller's daughter in a nearby village was to be married the following day and our presence at the event was absolutely imperative.

So here we were, picking our way through the slush to the bride's house accompanied by her sisters and followed by the eyes of interested neighbours who stood in their doorways observing us with unabashed curiosity. The fact that we had been summoned to assist the miller's daughter in preparing for the happiest day of her life suggested to me that we were no ordinary guests.

To my surprise, we arrived at what appeared to be a roomy cattle shed. I could hardly believe that we had come to the right place but, sure enough, we were ushered by the sisters through a low doorway to find ourselves in the company of two cows. The animals turned their heads to gaze at us with liquid brown eyes as they chewed the cud contentedly. The sound of grunting and an unmistakeable smell told us that there were also pigs rooting around somewhere in the semi-darkness. Puzzled, I turned to look at Anita but she just beamed at me brightly and we waded through the straw to the far end of the shed where there was another door. Behind this, a flight of rickety stairs led us up to the bride's home. I later learned that it was quite usual for village houses to be built in this way with accommodation for livestock at ground level and living quarters above. This made sense as the heat generated by the animals rose and so helped to warm the upper floor.

The bride's bedroom was full of people all fussing around her and offering advice.

"They're here! They're here!" cried the sisters in chorus and immediately all heads were turned in our direction as we walked into the room. The miller's daughter, a plump, apple-cheeked girl, sprang to her feet and kissed us both affectionately.

"This blouse," she said breathlessly, "do you think it's alright? It's the best I've got. And the skirt, do you think this grey one or the black?"

"The grey is perfect," Anita assured her, "and so is the blouse. But something must be done about your hair."

"Yes, I know. I was waiting for you."

Anita removed her coat in a business-like way and at once stepped into the role of hairdresser. She grabbed a handful of hairpins from the dressing table and thrust them into my hand with instructions to pass them to her as required. Deftly her fingers worked on the black shiny mane and soon it had been tamed into a neat coil at the back of her head. There were murmurs of approval from the bride's mother and other female relatives who stood watching us with keen interest. Two red carnations were poked through the coil and everyone agreed that the bride was now lovely to behold.

Next came the nylons and stiletto shoes, shiny and new for the occasion. Aware of the sorry state of Anita's and my legs and feet after the walk from the bus, my heart bled for her when I imagined how those immaculate shoes would look by the time we arrived at the church! Finally, a small, black veil of fine lace was draped carefully over her hair and, as a finishing touch, a few drops of the perfume 'Enchantment of Seville' were dabbed behind the dangling gold earrings. Everyone stood back to admire the final result of all this effort and the bride's mother, overcome by the beauty of her daughter, gave a little sob of delight and pressed a white lace handkerchief to her eyes.

Then there was the sound of people gathering in the street below and a few tuneless notes from a cornet could be heard. One of the sisters poked her head through the window then turned to us with a squeal of joy. "They've arrived! It's time to go."

After a quick, last minute glance at herself in the mirror, the bride, with great dignity, descended the stairs, crossed the cowshed and stepped out into the street, arm-in-arm with her godmother. The rest of us followed close behind.

Cheers rang out as she emerged to a tumultuous welcome from the assembled villagers. Happily, at that moment, the clouds parted and a little watery sunshine filtered through to illuminate the puddles between the ruts of mud and glinted on the brass instruments of the village band. A procession was forming and the band took up its position at the head followed by the bride and her relatives and then the rest of us.

After a few tentative hoots and honks, the band threw itself into an excruciating rendering of 'Here comes the Bride' with an enthusiasm and abandon that quite made up for its lack of musical skill. Behind it, the villagers sang as they splashed through the muddy puddles, dogs barked and chickens scattered at our approach while hordes of children ran alongside the band, shrieking with delight. In this joyful manner, we arrived at the church.

All I knew about the bridegroom was that his name was Manolo but now I saw him standing at the entrance, a well-built lad with a shock of bushy, black hair. He looked distinctly uncomfortable in what was probably a new suit, but his red face broke into a broad grin at the sight of his bride. With a final, triumphant roll of the drums, the procession halted and the bride joined her husband-to-be. The priest stood beside him and I realised, to my surprise, that the marriage ceremony was to take place then and there, on the church steps, presumably so that the entire village could witness it. There followed an hour-long nuptial mass inside the church during which the choir, alas, proved itself no more musical than the band.

When at last the happy couple emerged, now man and wife, into the strengthening sunlight, the waiting villagers at once set about the serious business of celebrating the occasion. Flagons and *porrónes* of wine were passed round, fireworks let off and the village band, having refreshed itself, struck up once more with renewed enthusiasm. Nobody cared whether or not it played in tune; it was the signal to begin dancing, and in no time everyone was prancing about, oblivious of the mud, laughing, shouting, singing and causing the chickens to rush hither and thither, dodging between flying legs and squawking in alarm. All the villagers joined in the fun, from tiny tots stomping and splashing happily in the puddles to the good-natured old folk who took this opportunity to exercise their stiffening joints.

Meanwhile, the bride and groom were having their photos taken outside the church. Unfortunately, the bride, overcome with emotion, had dissolved into tears and it was some time before she had composed herself sufficiently to face the camera. Anita and I were also called to pose with the couple alongside her parents, brothers and sisters, grandparents and *padrinos* (those overseeing the couple, rather as in the U.K. the best man looks after the bridegroom). The photo session over, the bridal party now joined the revels in the village square. At once everyone stopped dancing and stood aside. The cornet player announced that the next dance would be a *pasodoble* and there was an expectant silence as all eyes turned towards the bridegroom. Someone shouted, "Go on Manolo!" upon which the latter scratched his head and stood looking vaguely about him.

"What's he waiting for?" I whispered to Anita. "Why doesn't he lead off the dance with his bride?"

"Oh no, he won't do that," she replied in a low voice. "He has to choose someone else for the first dance and the one he chooses will have good luck. Everyone's waiting to see who he fancies."

Manolo took a thoughtful swig from his *porrón*, wiped his mouth on his sleeve, then, thrusting the *porrón* into someone's hand, turned on his heel and walked purposefully in our direction. Anita patted her hair and waited smugly for the inevitable. Amazingly, however, Manolo ignored her and instead grabbed me by the hand and pulled me to the centre of the square. The crowd cheered noisily, the band struck up and there was I, the Chosen One, dancing a *pasodoble* with him in front of the whole village. Dancing in stiletto heels was no easy matter in such thick mud. I fully expected to lose my shoes altogether and finish the dance barefoot, but by some miracle I just about managed to keep them on.

"You're not from round here, are you?" asked my partner as we danced. "You have a strange accent. Which part of Spain do you come from?"

I laughed. "Well, I'm not Spanish. I'm from England."

Manolo looked puzzled. "England? England? I've never heard of that place. Which part of Spain is that?"

I tried to explain to him that England was another country, far away, but I could see that I was getting nowhere. Fortunately, at that moment the dance ended saving us from further conversation.

At two in the afternoon, all the wedding guests assembled in an enormous barn where a mighty spread had been set out on trestle tables. Course after course arrived: first soup, then fish followed by vegetables, tortillas, meat, fruit and cheese. There seemed no end to the food which was accompanied by liberal quantities of the local wine. Towards the end of the meal, I could feel myself becoming increasingly drowsy to the point where I was turning over in my befuddled mind the possibility of creeping under the table for a surreptitious siesta.

By this time, most of the guests were seriously drunk and the bridal couple were being teased unmercifully with ribald suggestions and bawdy jokes. The bride blushed and Manolo spluttered with laughter, spilling wine down his best suit. The old men leaned across the table and joined in with reminiscences of their own wedding nights, eager to remind the younger ones that they too, their grandfathers, were once young and virile. Their wheezing laughter frequently exploded into fits of coughing and the oldest inhabitant nodded off halfway through his story, no doubt to dream himself back to those halcyon days.

At last, the meal, which had taken up most of the afternoon, came to an end. The older women bustled to and fro clearing away the plates and glasses while their men folk smoked and played dominoes. The other guests, including Anita and myself, staggered out into the fresh air to clear our heads and continue dancing. It need hardly be said that the band's playing was not improved by the intoxicated state of the players some of whom had difficulty in standing upright and had to be found chairs. However, despite all odds, the dancing did start up again and even merrier than before, for this time the wine had given some of the boys courage to seek out the girls of their choice. Several couples, having for a while escaped the constant scrutiny of their elders, managed to slip away into the dusk to seek blissful privacy in the cowsheds. Whispers, giggles and the odd little squeal could be heard behind the mud walls.

The merry-making continued until midnight when, unbelievably, we were expected to do justice to yet another enormous feast. No one's glass was allowed to remain empty, particular attention being given to the bridal couple. I was sitting opposite Manolo and I soon lost count of the number of glasses he was able to down, but I could see his eyes gradually glazing over while his bride threw him worried glances from time to time. It was easy to imagine what was passing through her mind and the misgivings she must have been feeling as she observed the increasingly paralytic state of her new husband.

By the end of the meal he was slumped senseless across the table and there was no way he could be sufficiently roused to make the short walk from the table to the taxi waiting to take the couple to Burgos. Eventually, his prostrate body had to be carried to the car where he was propped up like a rag doll in the corner, snoring loudly. The bride climbed in beside him, bravely trying to smile her thanks at the well-wishers who poked their heads through the window. As we watched the car bump away, amid cheers, into the darkness, I reflected that sadly, Manolo's wedding night would certainly not prove as memorable as those of his grandfathers.

A bus had been hired to take guests back to Burgos but the numbers had been greatly miscalculated for there was barely room for half of them. However, the men gallantly gave up their places inside the bus for us females while they clambered onto the roof still singing and draining the last bottles of wine. Typically, the bus refused to start and it took the driver a good hour of poking around under the bonnet, hampered by the curiosity and unwanted advice of the male passengers, before the engine could eventually be coaxed back to life.

"By the way," I asked Anita, between yawns, as we trundled out of the village and into the pitch-black Castilian night, "how did we get invited to that wedding?"

"Tell you tomorrow," she replied sleepily.

"Well, anyway, it was great fun…" I murmured and fell asleep. I never did discover the answer to my question.

CHAPTER NINE

MORE FRIENDS

For anyone who did not know Eduardo well, it would be impossible to believe that he suffered from haemophilia, for a more energetic, lively and cheerful young man would be difficult to find. Unfortunately, he had inherited a blood-clotting deficiency so that even a minor injury could lead to persistent, life-threatening bleeding. You might think that anyone with this condition would treat their bodies with meticulous care but alas, this was not the case with Eduardo. On the contrary, he was terrifyingly indifferent to his own welfare and would throw himself into every kind of strenuous physical activity regardless of the consequences. Add to this that he was accident-prone and it was not surprising that his twenty-five years of life had been punctuated by numerous spells in hospital. His long suffering family had long-since abandoned their efforts to protect him and were resigned to placing his life in the hands of the Virgin to whom they lit a candle every day.

I came to know Eduardo through my friend Julio, the one who had originally found me the job with Vázquez. There existed between these two, that special kind of love-hate relationship common to those who had known each other since infancy, shared the joys and frustrations of the school years, weathered together the traumas of adolescence and finally emerged, still friends, into adulthood. They were both extraordinary but very different characters: a truly bizarre pair. Julio was a fanatical anglophile and had persuaded his reluctant friend to spend several wet summers in the U.K. The last of these trips had been an absolute disaster as I was soon to learn.

Eduardo's job as a sales rep' for his father's small manufacturing firm in Logroño brought him regularly to Burgos, so I
was not surprised when one day I found him on our doorstep. He
had come to seek me out and discover what I had been up to,
probably on the instructions of Julio who exercised a curious
dominance over his friend, as he did with most of those around
him. This was something Eduardo resented bitterly but seemed
unable to remedy.

We drove in his ancient little car to the Espolón where, over
cups of coffee, he gave me his latest news.

"Julio is very annoyed with you. He says you haven't
answered his letters."

To my dismay, I realised this was true for I had not thought
much about Julio since leaving Vázquez's house and had not
written to let him know my new address.

"Oh! I forgot to tell him I'd left Vázquez. Anyway, how did
you know where to find me?"

"I went to that house and the maid said you had gone; but I
soon found out where you were. Everyone in Burgos seems to
know about you. Julio's coming back to Spain in a few days and I
bet he'll find some excuse to come to Burgos, so you can explain it
all to him then. He'll be livid of course that he's not been
constantly in your thoughts. You know what he's like!"

"Yes," I laughed, "thanks for the warning. Now, tell me about
yourself. How was your holiday in England?"

Eduardo exploded with laughter. "*Holiday*? That's not what
I'd call it. One hospital is much like another, you know."

"Hospital?"

"Yes. On the journey out there I was running up some steps
at Irún station carrying two suitcases and I tripped and twisted my
ankle. You should have seen my leg! It was like this!" He spread
out his hands, rocking with laughter. "It just wouldn't stop
swelling and Julio was in such a panic, thought I was going to pass
out on him or something. I don't know how we reached London.
I couldn't walk at all and Julio had to sort of carry me whenever
we changed trains. It was murder crossing Paris and he was *so
angry*! – said I'd ruined his holiday before it had begun. I suppose

he was right because we had to call an ambulance as soon as we arrived at Victoria and I spent the rest of the time in hospital. Anyway, it didn't really matter. It was pouring with rain the whole time and I saw all the sights last year."

"Eduardo, you're incorrigible. Why can't you be a bit more careful?"

He shrugged. "Not my fault. These things happen; but let's stop talking about me. How about tonight? I'm not leaving till tomorrow so we could do something together. How about the Sala de Fiestas? Why don't we go dancing?"

My heart sank. The thought of dancing with Eduardo filled me with dread. What if I were to tread on his toes?

"Oh no," I said hastily, "I don't really like dancing. Let's just take a stroll along the Espolón. We could have a drink at the Bar Gaona…"

"How *boring!*" interrupted Eduardo. "I'm sure you don't mean that. I know you really like dancing and that's what we'll do. The Sala de Fiestas it is. I've been there before and had a really good time."

"But your leg…"

"It's fine now. Meet you there at nine."

CﾃC ﾃｿ

I was not a particularly good dancer and the dances I was used to at home were not the ones popular in Spain. It was all Latin-American stuff, a nightmare for someone like me, unfamiliar with the complicated steps of the samba, rumba, cha-cha-cha, and so on. However, Eduardo knew them all and threw himself into their interpretation with great abandon. Desperately I tried to follow him, keeping my feet as far away from his as I could. Glancing down I could see the menacing stiletto heels of the other dancers flying through the air like daggers and often landing within a hair's breadth of my partner's vulnerable feet. It seemed incredible, as each nerve-racking dance came to an end that he was still unharmed for I fully expected the evening to culminate in an urgent call to the local hospital.

As we threaded our way back to our table after one such dance and I was feverishly trying to think up excuses for keeping him off the floor for the rest of the evening, I heard my name called and turning, managed to discern through the mass of bodies and haze of cigarette smoke, three familiar faces. Felipe was waving to us, his arm round Mari Carmen. Sergio was there too but seemingly without a partner and looking depressed.

"Come and join us!" yelled Felipe.

"Look Eduardo, there are some friends of mine. Let's go and sit with them!"

I grabbed his arm and dragged him over to their table, happy to have found the excuse I had been looking for. "I'd really like you to meet them."

"Haven't seen you for ages," said Sergio, "where have you been all this time?"

"Someone told me you had a *novio!*" giggled Mari Carmen. "That boy from the Isla..."

I quickly interrupted her. "The things people say! Now, you must meet my friend Eduardo from Logroño."

"Ah, Logroño," said Felipe clicking his fingers at a passing waiter. "Saw a very good bullfight there the summer before last. Antonio Ordoñez at his best. Won the ears and tails of both his bulls – fantastic performance. What will you have to drink? Blanco for both of you? Yes, also saw him at *San Fermín* last year. What a fiesta! I was running through the streets in front of the bulls with the best of them."

"Ah, now that's something I'd love to do!" exclaimed Eduardo enthusiastically, his eyes lighting up at the prospect. "Run with the bulls in Pamplona; perhaps next year..."

It finally came home to me that he was totally bent on self-destruction so I gave up worrying about him and started to enjoy the evening.

Eduardo, Felipe and Mari Carmen were talking bullfights but Sergio was bored and asked me to dance.

"She wouldn't come," he muttered miserably, his eyes gazing unseeingly ahead as we shuffled around. "I asked her but she wouldn't come."

I shook my head sympathetically knowing at once to whom he was referring.

"She's not interested in me at all," he continued and now I noticed that his speech was slightly slurred. "I keep trying, keep on hoping but she's just not interested. Do you know?" He turned his head to focus on me with some difficulty. "Do you know? She doesn't even *notice* me." His expression was that of a badly hurt child.

"I'm sorry," I said, not knowing how to respond but guessing it probably didn't matter as he was really talking to himself, not me.

"It's terrible feeling like this about someone. It's like an obsession and I can't think about anything else."

"Yes, I do know what you mean." Suddenly I felt I understood his problem.

"And can you imagine what it feels like?" He stopped dancing and we stood there in the middle of the floor while couples danced around us. "Have you any idea what it's like to care about someone as much as that and know the whole thing's hopeless?"

For some strange reason his words caused a cold fear to creep over me, the same inexplicable feeling of foreboding that I had felt several times recently. I tried to dismiss it but the uneasiness continued to haunt me for what remained of that night as I watched poor Sergio drowning his sorrows in alcohol.

႙ ႘

"After Christmas you must come and stay with my family for a long weekend. I want to show you Logroño. But for goodness sake don't tell Julio or I'll be in big trouble. I just want to see his face when you arrive."

Eduardo hooted with laughter as he climbed into his car and started the engine.

"Are you trying to get back at him for that miserable summer holiday?"

"Perhaps," he grinned. "Goodbye, I enjoyed last night. I'll look you up again next month when I'm back here. Watch out for

Julio! I guess he'll be seeking you out any day now. You've been warned!"

I watched his car bumping its way down the hill into the dazzling sunshine, raising a great cloud of dust in its wake as it turned into the road to Santander and was gone. I turned and walked back to the house, thinking about Julio as I collected my books for the morning's lessons. How well Eduardo knew his friend! Apart from his obsessions with England and of being an entrepreneur, the other outstanding feature of Julio's character was his possessive jealousy which made him an easy target for teasing. In view of Eduardo's warning I thought it wise to avoid seeing Luis for the next few days.

C&#x8; &#x8;O

The following Sunday morning, during a well-deserved lie-in, our dreams were rudely interrupted by someone shouting outside, under the bedroom window. Still half-asleep, Anita climbed out of the single bed we shared and staggered across the room, struggling into her dressing gown.

"*Oiga!*" yelled the voice under the window and I recognised it at once. Oh no! How typical! I buried my head under the covers.

Anita unlatched the heavy shutters and pushed them back to admit a stream of brilliant light. She opened the window and leaned out, the sun glinting on her tousled, black curls.

"*Que quiere usted?*" she called down. "What do you want?"

"The English girl," shouted the voice, "they told me she was here. Do you have an English girl staying here?"

"Yes, but we're in bed. Who are you?"

"I'm Julio Rivera. Her *novio*," replied the voice.

"That's a lie!" I groaned, surfacing unwillingly from sleep. "He lives in a fantasy world like Don Quixote! Tell him to come back later!"

But the voice under the window was now gabbling away non-stop, gathering speed and volume as it did so.

"In *bed*? At this time of day? Disgraceful! I can see she's already acquiring lazy Spanish habits. In London we don't stay in bed till ten o'clock. I've just come back from England and things are very different there. People get up early. Meals at sensible times: morning tea at half past seven; breakfast at eight. No wonder this country's going downhill. She should be ashamed of herself. In London she would have been up long ago—"

"Hush! You'll wake the neighbours," said Anita. "Wait there! I'll let you in."

She closed the shutters and groped for her slippers under the bed.

"I'll keep him quiet till you come down," she assured me. "You certainly have some odd friends."

As I hurriedly pulled on some clothes I could hear them in the kitchen below, Anita busying herself with coffee-making, Julio pacing restlessly to and fro, his voice rising to an excited crescendo.

"She is becoming *lazy* as we say in London." He used the English word "lazy" for he liked to sprinkle his conversation with English words presumably to impress the listener. "I am surprised at her. Only three months in Spain and she's becoming like the rest of us – I mean of you. I live like an Englishman now. Early to bed, early to rise. That's what they say in London and you should see how efficient they are over there. They get things done; not like here where everything's left till tomorrow. No. Appointments are kept on time. People don't arrive late for work, trains and buses run on schedule; you should see the difference!"

"Would you like some coffee?" I heard Anita saying. "She'll be down in a minute. Sit down please! All that pacing around is making me dizzy."

"We're still in the Middle Ages here, you know. Mules! Oxen! You don't find *those* in the streets of London. They have cars there. Everyone has a car. And a television. That's progress. People here don't know what progress is."

I stood for a moment outside the kitchen door listening to all this and trying hard not to shriek with laughter. When I walked in, having composed myself, I beheld the lean figure of Julio pacing restlessly up and down. He immediately stopped in his tracks in the middle of the kitchen, face flushed, dark hair awry, black eyes darting all over the place. Anita was smiling and humming a little tune as she poured the coffee. She threw me a quick side-long glance of amusement as though to say whatever next will you bring into this house?

"Hello Julio," I said. "Great to see you. You're up bright and early."

He straightened his tartan tie, the one he bought in London and wore all the time, and cleared his throat.

"You call this early? *Dios mío!* Why in Lon..."

"Yes, yes," I interrupted, "don't go over all that again! As a matter of fact this leisurely Spanish life style rather suits me."

"That's obvious!" Julio took a gulp of his coffee. "Now hurry up! We've wasted enough time. Get your coat on! We're going out. I've something very important to tell you."

Anita and I sat down to enjoy our coffee while Julio resumed his pacing like a frustrated caged beast, pausing only occasionally to run his fingers through his hair and glare at us in exasperation as we unhurriedly finished our breakfast. However, sounds of Teo and Auntie Domi stirring above prompted me to fetch my coat before our visitor had time to break his temporary brooding silence. Anita winked at me as I hurried him through the door.

Out in the street, he grabbed me roughly by the arm. "What are you doing in that house? What on earth have you been up to? I had a terrible time finding you. You weren't at Vázquez's place and they wouldn't tell me where you'd gone. Why did you leave after all the trouble I took finding you a job? And why haven't you written to me all this time? Is there somebody else?" His eyes narrowed with suspicion. "If there is I'll kill him! You know you're MY *niña.*"

Patiently I explained to him all the events that led to my present situation except, of course, the bit about Vázquez trying to gain access to my bed as I didn't want to see Julio arrested for murder. By the time I had finished my story he was exploding with anger.

"That man's a villain!" he shouted, gesticulating wildly. "I'm going to see him about this right now. I'll see he pays you the money he owes you. Just wait till I get hold of him!"

It was with the utmost difficulty that I managed to restrain him from bursting into Vázquez's house then and there and creating an ugly scene.

However, he eventually calmed down after I explained that it had all worked out for the best and Vázquez now had to live with the embarrassing fact that his English teacher had left his house but was still living in Burgos.

We entered one of the cafes in the Espolón and sat down by a window. I wanted to know what matter of great importance he had to impart to me. His face lit up at the mention of it.

"Look!" He rubbed a clear patch in the steamed-up window. "Do you see that?"

I peered through the glass and spotted an ostentatious American car, its excessive length spread over the pedestrian area opposite the café. It looked thoroughly out of place parked there, under the trees, with its flashy chrome plating and enormous headlights: like some alien object dropped from outer space.

Julio demanded to know if I liked it. "It's big, isn't it? And expensive?"

I nodded. I found cars rather boring but he had to be humoured.

"Well," He reached for my hand and held it between both of his. "One day I shall have one just as big and twice as expensive. You see, I'm going to be rich. Very rich."

This comment did not come as a surprise to me as he was always thinking up grandiose schemes for making money. Not for him some mundane job; he was going to become a self-made millionaire. To this end he had already sunk most of his savings in various futile projects but his lack of success did not deter him in any way from pursuing his dream.

"Oh yes, so what is it this time?"

"Heels." He lowered his voice mysteriously and looked about him as though seeking out some spy who might be lurking in the shadows, eager to poach his new money-making secret. "Steel caps for stilettos. I saw them in England. There's nothing like them here. They prevent narrow heels from wearing down. I'm onto a real winner here. I can't lose."

I was doubtful. "You've had these schemes before," I reminded him.

"But this is something altogether different. I'll borrow the money and start manufacturing them in Logroño. And I'll launch a huge publicity campaign – 'steel heel caps will bring double life to your stiletto shoes' – that sort of thing. Yes, I shall soon be running a most successful business and then, later, I shall expand. Market them in Venezuela. There's no end to the possibilities. You'll see. Very soon I'll be rich."

He seemed so delighted with his new idea that I hadn't the heart to voice my own thoughts on the subject which were that fashions come and go and the days of stiletto heels were probably numbered.

"I saw Eduardo the other day," I said, trying to distract him from this new obsession. "He told me about his terrible holiday in England."

"Careless idiot!" snapped Julio. "It was all his own fault. He's always doing stupid things and landing himself in hospital. And how about me? I had to practically carry him all the way to London."

"You could have been a bit more sympathetic; after all he is your best friend and he's got such an awful problem."

"But he's a fool. He ruined my holiday in England. Anyway, what was he doing sneaking down here and seeing my *novia* on his own?"

"How many more times? I'm NOT your *novia*!"

Julio looked at his watch, ignoring my protest.

"I've got to go. I have a train to catch. I must be back in Logroño tonight. I only stopped over here on my way back from Madrid and tomorrow morning I've a meeting with someone about my business."

He carried on talking incessantly about his project all the way to the station. I noticed he had bought himself a briefcase and was already trying to acquire the appearance of a successful businessman.

We arrived at the station with only a few minutes to spare and indeed, the approaching train could be heard in the distance as he bought his ticket. He frowned down at me, his dark eyes smouldering.

"I want to kiss you." he announced suddenly, dragging me into a corner.

"But the train's coming!"

"I want to kiss my *niña*."

He threw down his briefcase and pounced on me like a cat on its prey. Julio kissed in much the same way as he spoke: fast, furiously and non-stop. The train was pulling into the station but he appeared to have forgotten about his important business appointment.

"You'll miss it," I gasped, trying to extricate myself from his vice-like embrace. "You'll miss the train and your appointment tomorrow. It's terrible the way you inefficient Spaniards never keep appointments on time."

Julio started, threw me aside, grabbed his briefcase and bounded out of the shadows and into the train like a streak of lightning just as the stationmaster waved his flag.

"Here! I've a present for you," he shouted from the open window as the train moved off. "Catch!"

He tossed me a small packet which I caught while running alongside the train.

"*Adiós, niña!*"

His dark head disappeared into the carriage as the train snaked away. I looked down at the object in my hand. Carefully I opened it and extracted two small pieces of metal stuck to a card bearing the legend:

FOR THE ELEGANT WOMAN. JULIO RIVERA'S
STEEL CAPS FOR STILETTO SHOES

CHAPTER TEN

COUSIN BEA AND CHORIZOS

We were now well into November and the weather was becoming increasingly cold. There were frequent flurries of snow and the bitter mountain winds returned with a vengeance. It was always such a relief to return to the warmth of Anita's kitchen after my last lesson of the day. Here, the heat generated by the cooking stove and the *brasero,* (a container of smouldering charcoal placed under the table) was augmented by the volume of people who usually packed the room.

I noticed that several relatives had suddenly come to stay at the house. First, there was Anita's cousin, Margarita. She was the daughter of that uncle who had somehow managed to escape the fate of his brothers and had fled to France towards the end of the Civil War. He made his home there, in the French Pyrenees which divided him from his native land: the land to which he was destined never to return. However, he settled down well and raised two beautiful daughters, Margarita and Blanquita. Unlike their exiled father, the girls were able to return regularly to Spain and, on reaching adolescence, they both acquired Spanish *novios* to whom they remained remarkably faithful despite long absences.

On this occasion, Margarita had come for a short stay to be with her *novio,* a smiling young man called Jacinto, and the house was all the brighter for her presence. Everything about her exuded cheerfulness and vitality, from her exotic gypsy looks and flamboyant style of dressing to the lusty sound of her rich flamenco voice raised in song as she toiled over the washing in Domi's sink. Her firm, young arms, bronzed even at this time of year, would plunge in and out of the lather in time to her singing which resounded through the house.

In addition, we were at that time host to Domi's Cousin Bea and her family on one of their regular visits. Bea was the true country cousin who lived in a remote village some miles from Burgos with her husband, Jaime, the village school master, and their daughter, Marta, an only child. When they came to see us they nearly always brought something from the country such as those memorable cockerels in the lavatory, but this time, to our relief, her offering consisted of nothing more formidable than a home-made cheese. The purpose of her visit, as she soon made clear, was to persuade Aunt Domi to return with her to the village the following weekend in order to help her with the preparation of *chorizos*. They had fattened a fine pig, the best, she assured us, to be found in the entire neighbourhood and it was now ready for slaughter. It would provide *chorizos*, the spicy sausage so typical of Spain, for the rest of the year, not to mention *morcillas* (blood sausage). Clearly, she could not, single-handed, undertake all the work involved in making them so she had come to fetch Domi.

Aunt Domi did not seem too happy with the idea. She had enough on her plate already, she grumbled, and was disinclined to leave her house and 'children' for a whole weekend. Cousin Bea brushed aside her objections, pointing out that Margarita was quite capable of looking after the house and cook for Teo, and as for Anita and me, well, why not bring us with her? The country air would do us good, we could help with the chorizos and there would be plenty to entertain us. Every Saturday night there was a dance for the young people in the village. Yes, that would be the best solution.

So it was that the following Saturday found us bright and early waiting for the train to take us to the nearest station to Bea's village. I had to cancel my classes for that day but I didn't mind. After my amusing experiences at the recent wedding, I was curious to find out more about Spanish rural life.

Bea had gone home the day before to organise the slaughter of the pig so that it would be ready for when we arrived. Her village, she told me, was really two villages, one on a hill and the other down in the neighbouring valley. Legend had it that a secret underground passage ran from the church on the hill to somewhere down in the lower village but no one had managed to discover it. This all sounded rather intriguing.

When we arrived at the station it was pouring with rain and we seemed to be in the middle of nowhere. Clutching our bags, we set out across the fields, squelching in the mud and stumbling over ruts and through puddles. The bleak meseta stretched out before us, a flat, treeless wilderness with no shelter anywhere and the driving rain was soaking us to the skin. I longed for wellies as my leather lace-ups gradually became saturated.

"How much further?" I enquired of Anita between chattering teeth, after staggering along for about a quarter of an hour.

She laughed. "There's a long way to go yet," was her reply and she was right. Our trek lasted about an hour although Anita assured me it would have taken less time but for the mud. At last, the small hill containing half the village came into sight, just visible through the gloom and pounding rain which was fast turning to sleet. Despite the fact that we were all freezing cold and soaked through, Aunt Domi never complained. She battled on before us, beating a trail, like an Arctic explorer. Amazingly, she knew her way despite there being absolutely no landmarks. The sight of her small, dark figure forging ahead inspired us to keep going as she ploughed her way defiantly through the inhospitable landscape, clutching her drenched shopping bag and several strings of garlic. We struggled along behind as best we could, like two bedraggled sheep following their shepherdess, confident that she knew where she was going and would lead us, eventually, to shelter.

CB EO

The best end of the village, apparently, was the part that stood on the hill. Here lived the more important members of the community such as the priest, the *guardia civil* and the school master, Bea's husband. The house stood close to the village school and was built of mud and stone with small barred windows and a roof of curved, terracotta tiles. Adjoining the house was a large cattle shed surrounded by a cobbled yard, slippery with mud and dung. A number of chickens were grubbing around but they scattered, spraying us with mud, as a bedraggled dog approached.

Cousin Bea stood beaming in the doorway, pleased to see that despite all odds, we had in fact turned up to help her with the chorizos. She gathered us up and bundled us into the warm haven of her farmhouse kitchen, relieving us of our belongings and calling to Marta to bring out a bottle of *anís*. Our sodden clothes hung from us like limp rags, dripping pools of water onto the tiles. We were numb with cold and exhausted but Cousin Bea and Marta fussed around us, helping to peel off our outer garments and remove our mud-caked shoes, while plying us with *anís* to revive our bodies and spirits after our ordeal.

Bea hung the wet clothes from various hooks in the ceiling close to the charcoal stove and alongside strings of onions and great strips of raw meat belonging, presumably, to the unfortunate prize pig that had met its fate the day before.

Anita and I sank gratefully down at the table, feeling the delicious warmth of the *brasero* embracing our bare legs and watching Bea and Aunt Domi discussing the best way to set about preparing the chorizos. On and on they went, interrupting each other and gesticulating wildly, Domi's shrill voice vying with that of Cousin Bea. Anyone not understanding Spanish would have assumed that they were having a fierce argument. Fascinated, I watched how Bea would spread her hands dramatically across her chest, rolling her eyes heavenward and, from time to time, run her fingers through the stray wisps of hair that had escaped from her bun. Her gestures reminded me so much of a Murillo Madonna that I half-expected to see a cluster of cherubs gather above her head!

I liked Cousin Bea. I knew that beneath those generous, heaving bosoms lay a heart of gold. It was she who always rallied to our assistance at times of emergency such as when there was illness in the house. Yes, I liked her a lot and was glad we had come to help her with the chorizos.

The *anís* went down very well. In the region of Burgos it was always considered the standard remedy for cold and I was frequently offered a glass before going out to my classes in the morning. We sipped it slowly, savouring its sweet, aniseed flavour and enjoying its warm glow as it slipped down our throats. Domi and Bea were still discussing the chorizos.

"Have you got enough garlic? And how about the girl? Is the girl coming to help us this afternoon?"

"She'll be here when she's needed."

They were referring to one of the village girls who helped Bea in the house. I had seen this girl before as sometimes she accompanied Bea to Burgos. She was a buxom teenager with well-rounded hips and breasts and rosy cheeks. I had a sneaking feeling that Jaime had more than a passing interest in her.

"There's not a minute to be lost," remarked Domi. "We must have an early lunch and get started straight away."

"That's right. Not a minute to be lost," echoed Bea. "There's all this meat to deal with and I've got a bucket of blood in the pantry for *morcillas*."

Suddenly, I didn't feel so hungry for that early lunch.

○3　80

One of the things I was quick to discover about Spanish village life was that there were no such things as lavatories; at least not in the conventional sense of the word. Being unable to find anything remotely resembling one anywhere in the house, I asked Anita what I should do as Nature's urge increased. She smiled and told me to ask Bea to show me the way. Ah yes, I thought, an outside loo of course. It's still the same with some old cottages in England. However, I was not a little surprised when Bea hurried me from the house to the adjoining cowshed and pushed me into its dark, smelly interior.

"Over there," she said in a matter-of-fact voice. I peered into the gloom looking for a door to the loo but, so far as I could see, there wasn't one; just four stone walls, a lot of straw, two enormous brindled cows and a few chickens.

Puzzled, I turned again to Bea. "Where?" I queried.

"Why, over in that corner, there. Not this end where the animals are. Oh, and mind the chickens!"

So saying she disappeared and I was left alone with the cows which raised their great heads and eyed me with some interest. For a moment we stood staring at each other while I plucked up sufficient courage to cross the shed to the appropriate corner. This must be what life was like in medieval times, I thought to myself while using the corner with considerable distaste and not a little apprehension as the cows had decided to accompany me and I noticed they had very long, sharp horns. They stood close by and I tried to ignore them, but I could hear the sound of their munching jaws and feel their warm breath on the back of my neck. Also, as my eyes grew accustomed to the semi-darkness, I saw that beside the hens pecking at my feet, a row of them sat roosting on a nearby rafter so care had to be taken to avoid this additional hazard. By comparison with all this, the cockerels in Domi's lavatory seemed but a minor inconvenience.

After this little adventure, I returned to the kitchen where the chorizo-making was now in full swing. Anita and I started to prepare the garlic and rice for the *morcillas* while Domi, Bea and the girl were busy with the meat. Jaime sat at the table, watching the proceedings and I noticed how his eyes followed the girl as she went about her work. She was looking as comely as ever and was wearing a tight, low-cut jumper which showed off her figure particularly well whenever she leaned across the table for another piece of meat. Each time this happened Jaime's eyes would dilate with approval. She was well aware of this and sometimes threw him sly glances, tossing her head coquettishly. Fortunately, Bea did not notice as she was far too busy giving orders and directing operations. In fact, she was barely aware of her husband's presence. He was everything that she was not: small, slim, shy and unobtrusive but despite being completely over-shadowed by his dominating and extrovert wife, I guessed that this man had hidden depths.

We worked till eight in the evening when Bea suggested that Anita and I should stop and get ourselves ready for the village dance and we were glad of an excuse to get away from the heat and odours of the kitchen. Although Anita warned me that this dance didn't promise to be a particularly exciting experience, we both thought it would be amusing.

It took us some time to clean sufficient mud from our shoes to make them look reasonably presentable. For all their lack of glamour, we had elected to wear them so as not to ruin our precious stilettos, remembering how they had suffered at the village wedding.

Happily, the rain had stopped by the time we were ready to leave but the slippery mud made our descent to the lower village both difficult and dangerous. We slithered and stumbled along clinging to each other, trying to avoid the larger puddles and wondering why we had bothered to clean our shoes. From the crumbling cottages that lined our route, other young people were emerging in twos or threes: dark, moving shapes in the misty stillness of the night. We could hear the girls chattering excitedly, the smell of their cheap perfume mingling with the all-pervading stench of dung.

By the time we arrived the dance had already begun. It was held in a dilapidated barn with a rickety floor and chairs lining the walls. At one end of the room the village band was making a brave but rather unsuccessful attempt at playing 'España Cañí'. Their musical skill was no better than that of the band at the wedding, but we had to admire their enterprise. For isolated communities without radios or record players, the local band was an essential ingredient of village life and nobody cared how they played.

Few people were dancing. Oddly, the girls were all sitting lined up against the wall while the boys sat opposite staring at them. They were all wearing their best clothes, the boys looking uncomfortable in faded suits, their hair plastered to their heads with grease, their red, work-stained hands spread awkwardly across their knees. The girls wore tight dresses and bright red lipstick. Anita and I hesitated momentarily, not knowing quite what to do, then we made our way over to the girls' side and sat down, wondering what would happen next.

The band struck up a new tune and two of the girls wandered out onto the middle of the floor and started dancing together. They were quickly followed by another pair until the whole floor was filled with dancing girls while the boys remained obstinately rooted to their seats. Anita and I looked at each other and tried hard to suppress our giggles.

"Well, I'll tell you something," she whispered, "I'm not dancing with *you!*"

She let out a little shriek of laughter and the other girls turned round to stare. At last, one of the shy males opposite managed to pluck up sufficient courage to make a move. Tugging nervously at the unfamiliar tie which imprisoned his neck and smoothing back his shiny hair, he rose hesitantly to his feet, looked around at the dancing girls then, stepping forward with sudden determination, he tapped one of them on the shoulder, disengaged her from her female partner and slid her into his arms. Encouraged by his boldness, several others immediately did the same and we soon realised this was the accepted routine. Anita and I watched these goings-on with increasing amazement as we sat waiting to see if any of them would have enough confidence to approach us. None of them did, so we remained wallflowers for the rest of the evening although some of the boys ogled us with open-mouth curiosity making us feel like aliens.

"Oh well," yawned Anita as we made our way back up the hill, "we didn't miss much. They're the most boring lot I've ever seen."

CB BO

Supper that night was an enormous bowl of chick peas accompanied by lumps of thick, white pork fat followed by grilled mutton chops. Bea spent some time trying to force this enormous meal down her reluctant husband who said he wasn't feeling hungry. She nagged and bullied him, complaining that if he didn't eat up he would surely waste away; there was precious little of him as it was. Her loud voice ground away in a ceaseless flow as she piled yet more onto his plate, poking him occasionally with her fork to keep his attention. But Jaime wasn't listening to her. The words went straight over his head as he sat there staring vacantly, his mind probably on other things.

"*Jaime!*" screamed his wife. "Do you hear what I'm saying? Eat, man, eat!"

He picked up his fork with a deep sigh and held it poised

above his plate for some minutes, contemplating the chick peas with gloomy distaste. Then, with another sigh, he settled down to pick at them, muttering inaudibly under his breath. With a nod of satisfaction, Bea turned her attention to Marta (who was a carbon copy of her father in both looks and temperament), shovelling mountains of chick peas onto her plate, oblivious of her loud protests. Bea plonked the great cooking pot down on the table and appealed to us for sympathy in her dilemma. "What am I to do with such a family? I have two skeletons to feed and this is what I get all the time. Soon there will be nothing left of them and the neighbours will say that I've been starving them to death."

I decided that it would be wise to finish the chick peas down to the last crumb, which I managed to do with some difficulty but I could not bring myself to tackle the pork fat – much to Bea's disappointment.

By early afternoon the following day the clouds were beginning to gather again, rolling across the plain, dark and forbidding, threatening to make our homeward trudge across the fields as unpleasant as that of the day before. Aunt Domi peered anxiously at the sky and decided that we should leave immediately. The chorizo-making was now well under way so our help was no longer essential. Bea said she understood but would have preferred us to stay a little longer. There was still much to be done and, strangely, the girl hadn't turned up that afternoon which she couldn't understand. I noticed Jaime was also missing.

The return walk to the station was a race against time and weather with the clouds chasing us all the way, blown in our direction by an icy wind. The station just came into sight as the heavens opened. However, we had made the journey in record time and just managed to catch an earlier train to Burgos. As we rattled along in the freezing carriage, the rain lashing against the windows, Anita and I reviewed our weekend. We both felt we would have liked a bit more time there: time to explore both villages properly and perhaps find some clue to the mystery of the secret tunnel.

"I don't believe it exists," said Anita, "I think it's just a legend."

"Perhaps it does exist but not many people know about it. Imagine living in an isolated place like that with everyone knowing each other's business! It would be the ideal refuge for people wanting to hide themselves away from the neighbours."

"What sort of people?"

"People who want to be alone together, away from prying eyes."

"You mean – like secret lovers?"

"Something like that."

We both knew who we had in mind.

CHAPTER ELEVEN

THE END OF A DREAM

I knew they were his footsteps. I could have distinguished them if a whole army had been marching along the Espolón instead of a few hardy souls braving the bitter wind that bleak winter's afternoon.

The footsteps were coming closer behind me, quickening their pace but, this time, they did not fill me with excitement and happiness. Instead I felt only dread and tension, the sickening kind that precedes an unpleasant ordeal.

The day after Julio's fleeting visit, I had seen Luis at Federico's academy. As soon as I walked into the room I could sense that something was very wrong. Throughout the whole of our lesson he was silent, his eyes avoiding mine. When it was over, Don Federico, jovial as usual, invited us to join him in the Bar Paloma but Luis declined.

"What is the matter with you two today? You both have such long faces," observed our teacher.

"I have a lot on my mind," muttered Luis, "quite a few problems."

"Ah!" Federico switched momentarily to English. "*When sorrows come, they come not single spies but in battalions.* Hamlet, Act four, Scene five. Now, have a drink with me. It will make you feel better."

Luis shook his head. "Thank you, but we have to go." He took my arm and we hurried out into the street.

"What was all that about?" I asked. "What's the matter with you?"

"I just can't face the Bar Paloma – or Federico's small talk. Not today."

We walked back towards Anita's house, he chain-smoking, his eyes fixed on the pavement.

Eventually I said, "You have to tell me. We can't go on like this."

"Yes, I know."

Suddenly, he stopped, pulling me aside, and we stood facing each other. He took me by the shoulders, his eyes searching my face anxiously.

"*Vida mía*, something has happened. Something you have to know."

"Yes, alright. Tell me!" I felt unable to bear the maddening suspense any longer. "Do you think I haven't noticed lately that something's wrong? That you have 'something on your mind' as you told Don Federico? I need to know everything."

There followed an agonizing silence during which I could see him wrestling with indecision. At last he released me and turned away, passing a hand across his forehead.

"I can't," he said. "Not now. I will tell you but not yet. Not here. On Sunday afternoon we'll meet by the Hotel España at three. We'll walk up to the monastery and I'll tell you then. Now I have to think. *Hasta luego*." He kissed me briefly, squeezed my hand, turned and was gone.

I was left feeling stunned, sick with apprehension: like someone under sentence of execution awaiting the firing squad. But the fateful afternoon had now arrived and here I was, in the Espolón, attending that ominous rendez-vous. For a moment I was seized by the temptation to run away and mingle with the other strollers to escape what lay ahead, – but it was too late for now I felt his hand on my arm.

I turned to look at him and was shocked by his appearance. His handsome face was ashen-grey and there were dark rings under his eyes. Had he really been cured of his tuberculosis I wondered, or would he suddenly collapse and die in my arms like some character from a Victorian melodrama?

We walked together in silence, first by the river and then, leaving the town, we climbed the lonely hill up towards the monastery. He took my hand and we braced ourselves against the biting wind. It whistled through the tall poplars lining the road, tearing the last leaves from their skeletal branches, its mournful wail a fitting accompaniment to our anguished thoughts. For an hour we walked on saying little. It was obvious that he was more than reluctant to talk about the matter that was 'on his mind' and I was equally reluctant to press him. We were both cowards, trying to put off the inevitable for just for a little longer.

Then the monastery came in sight and we stopped to gaze at the bleak, wintry landscape surrounding it. On the horizon, silhouetted against the ragged sky, a solitary monk was ploughing with a wooden hand plough and a pair of oxen, his brown habit blowing about him, his feet bare but for a pair of rope-soled sandals. I couldn't imagine how cold he must have felt. This was an image from another age so perhaps Julio was right about Spain.

"What a hard life they have," I remarked, "and they're not even allowed to speak."

Luis shrugged. "It's the life they choose."

"But there's nothing to stop you speaking so why are you behaving like a Trappist monk?"

Luis shook his head in a gesture of hopelessness. "I don't know how to begin. You see, I have deceived you and I've deceived myself too." He paused.

"Go on!" I urged.

He drew me into his arms. "I love you. You must believe that."

A strange numbness crept over me, like a self-induced anaesthetic. "Go on!" I repeated, surprised at my own calm. "Or would it be easier if I said it for you? It's the Institute gardener's daughter, isn't it?"

I felt him flinch but I didn't look up. I didn't want to see his face at that moment. Instead, I closed my eyes and clung to him believing this to be the last time I would feel his arms around me.

"How did you know?" he gasped. "I suppose I was a fool to think I could keep it from you. But she's been away. She's a nurse and she's been in Madrid looking after an aunt of hers who is very ill. All this time she's been away and now she's coming back to Burgos – tomorrow, in fact. I just don't know what to do."

"Do you love her?" I asked in a dull voice.

"I thought I did, until I met you. Now she means nothing to me. Nothing at all. Please believe me. You're the only one I can love and that's the truth. Tomorrow, when I see her, I shall tell her it's all over between us. Finished!"

I thought, poor girl! How terrible to have loved Luis perhaps for years, not just months, and then to suffer such a blow, such a humiliation! How would I feel if I were her, believing myself secure in his love all this time, waiting for him to come out of the sanatorium, confident of our future together and then, suddenly, after a few weeks absence in the noble cause of nursing a sick aunt, to come home to this? Cast aside for some foreign girl with whom he had become infatuated. I knew how I would feel and I couldn't wish it on anyone. Besides, how could I be sure now that he really did love me? It might indeed be just a passing fancy in which case my fate could be the same as hers. All at once it struck me that I was fed up with being in love. It now felt like being caught in a trap like a rat, a slave to overpowering emotions. Suddenly, I wanted to be free again. The whole thing was becoming too complicated and too exhausting. I was angry with him for having deceived me, making me live in a fool's paradise, and now the time had come to rub Puck's lethal potion out of my eyes.

All this time, while these thoughts were racing through my head, I was vaguely aware that Luis was caressing me, kissing me, and talking, but I didn't hear his words.

Reluctantly I drew myself away from him, took a deep breath and said: "Listen Luis! What you have just told me makes it easier for me to break something to you. I'm afraid you're not the only one who's been deceitful. Perhaps that will make you feel better. You see, I have someone else too. I knew him in London and he helped me to come to Burgos. I forgot about him when I met you, just like you forgot your girlfriend, but last week he came back to Spain and we've been seeing each other again."

I paused to see what effect my words were having. Luis was staring at me aghast, his green eyes wide open, shining in his pale face like two strange jewels. "So it was true," he whispered, "Paco was right."

I continued with my lies. "I realize now that I've seen him again that I really do love him and what I felt for you before has gone. He's very jealous so he must never know about us. I think it would be best if we stopped seeing each other."

Luis seized me by the wrist and tugged me towards him. "Who is it?" he demanded in a strangled voice. "Another Spaniard?"

I nodded. "His name's Julio but he's not from Burgos. That's all I can tell you."

"Paco saw you with someone in the Espolón, someone dark with a loud voice. Was that him?"

"Yes."

He groaned and leaned against a tree, burying his head in his arm. "And I didn't believe him. I thought he was joking," he said bitterly.

He looked so dejected I longed to rush over to him, embrace him, tell him it was all a lie. Instead, I took his arm and said gently, "It was wonderful while it lasted: like a dream; but it's over now. You must go back to your girlfriend and I to Julio. We have to wake up and, whatever happens, *they* mustn't know about *us*."

By now it was becoming dark and bitterly cold and we were both shivering. Luis was still leaning against the tree, staring out across the fields like one in a trance. I suggested we should start walking back for I was anxious to end this wretched afternoon. He came out of his reverie and lit a cigarette. Then we made our way back down the hill, beneath the ghostly army of naked poplars swaying against the darkening sky. We neither spoke nor looked at each other as we walked side by side, each wrapped in a cloak of silent misery. We did not touch each other. The bond between us had been irreparably broken.

I wanted to leave him at the cathedral but, as though wishing to prolong the agony, he insisted on accompanying me right the way home. By the time we reached the house it had started to snow, the great white flakes landing on our faces. Now that the moment had come to say our last goodbyes, I felt dizzy and slightly sick.

Suddenly, Luis broke the dreadful silence. "You don't mean

what you said – about this Julio. You don't really mean it, do you?" His voice was soft and it was all I could do to fight back the tears. Was I then such an unconvincing liar? "I need you," he was saying, "I want you with me in Madrid. Tomorrow I'll explain everything to Maruja – *please*, try to forgive me!"

"Don't say anything more!" I begged. "You're making it worse for both of us. Just go away and don't say another word."

"Alright!" he hissed. "I'll go. But remember this! It's not over. It's not over between us and it never will be."

With this he turned quickly away and disappeared into the swirling snowstorm. For a moment I remained there, rooted to the spot, the snow flakes mingling with my copious tears. I heard the door opening behind me and Anita calling from the house.

"Come on in! You'll freeze to death. What on earth are you doing standing out there in the cold?" Hastily, I rubbed my face and ran indoors.

"Just look at all that snow!" laughed Anita. "Winter's here."

"Yes," I whispered, glancing back once more at the freezing, empty street before shutting the door, "winter's here alright."

CHAPTER TWELVE

THE DAUGHTERS OF THE CAPTAIN GENERAL

Of all the emotions to which the young and vulnerable are subject, perhaps one of the cruellest is that of disappointed love, particularly when experienced for the first time. At nineteen there has not been time to build around oneself that armour of philosophical stoicism, which, in later life, protects the ego to some extent from painful experiences. Not being sufficiently strong to bear on my own the agony of a broken heart, I confided my troubles in Anita and, for the next few nights, bored her with my sufferings as we lay together in our cramped single bed, I sobbing inconsolably into the pillow. Unfortunately, I did not find in her a very sympathetic listener.

"You can't say I didn't warn you," she remarked cheerfully. "I told you right from the start that he was going around with the Institute gardener's daughter but you wouldn't listen. If you will go poaching on other people's territory what do you expect? Oh, do stop crying! You're making the pillow soggy."

"But I never really thought he had a *novia*."

"Anyway, you're well rid of him. I can't imagine what you saw in him in the first place."

"I love him."

"You're mad."

" I can't help it."

"He has nothing to commend him apart from his looks."

"How do you know? You don't know him."

"Bah! All these good lookers are the same. So vain! They

think they can have their way with any girl they fancy. Personally, I don't care about looks, it's character that counts."

"Huh? You're a fine one to talk! How about that handsome boyfriend of yours?"

"Boyfriend? What boyfriend? I haven't any boyfriend."

"Of course you have. The one from Oviedo."

"Oh *him*! I gave him up ages ago. His letters were getting so boring. No, I'm fancy free – we both are now and that means we can have some fun when we get to Andalusia." She laughed merrily at this happy thought and added, full of excitement: "They say the Andalusians are *very* romantic. So forget that stupid Luis, there are plenty more fish in the sea."

CB BO

The snow had melted leaving all the unmade-up roads, including ours, in a terrible condition. Cartwheels and hooves had churned them into a sea of mud and the numerous potholes had formed great puddles everywhere. Negotiating these roads was no easy matter for pedestrians but trial and error, together with the discomfort of teaching English for three hours with wet feet, had taught me to work out the best route into town. This I was now following. The air was icily cold still and a thin, white mist hung over everything, giving a ghostly appearance to the peasants trundling by in their mule-drawn carts, piled high with produce for the market.

As I picked my way round the puddles I was thankful for the warm socks Anita's brother had lent me. I had only brought summer clothes with me from England, and apart from a few garments purchased locally, was ill-equipped to face the hard, Castilian winter.

However, there were plenty of others far worse off. The grinding poverty ever present in Spain became even more apparent in winter. Ragged children, their small, thin limbs blue with cold ran around in packs, like stray dogs, begging for money. Women and children could frequently be seen scratching through rubbish dumps and hardly a day went by without some poor old woman or cripple knocking on our door. These desperate people knew which households were sympathetic to their plight and would call again and again even though we could not afford to give each more than a few *céntimos*. The memory of one such woman haunted me for days. She called on a wild, dark night and stood in the doorway, her body bent double with age, one gnarled hand clutching her thin black shawl against the cruel wind, the other fingering a rosary. She didn't ask for money but just stood there shivering, her lips moving in silent prayer. She no doubt realised that just the sight of her piteous condition would be sufficient to stir our hearts to charity.

My route took me past the bullring, forlorn and deserted at this time of year, its creaking, shabby doors thrown open to reveal the empty arena. The damp sand still bore faint traces of the dramas that had taken place there not so long ago. A group of small boys rushed past me and tumbled into the ring, shouting and playing at being bullfighters.

Hurrying on, I reached the rickety little bridge that had to be crossed with care as there were several planks missing. There, to my surprise, I saw Don Federico puffing away at one of his self-rolled cigarettes and watching a group of labourers who were working among a great pile of stones.

"Why, Freddie, what are you doing here?" I called to him, wondering why he wasn't in one of his bars.

"They are pulling down the city walls," he complained grimly indicating the workmen with his cigarette. "Look over there!" He nodded towards the heap of stones. "That used to be part of the city walls and they pull it down for new buildings. They are destroying our heritage. Is terrible."

I sympathised and told him the same thing was happening all the time in England.

"What is happening to this ancient city? Capital of Castile! Home of the Catholic Kings! So much history violated! Is a disgrace. Come! I cannot bear to see it. Let's go to see! Why don't we have a *chato*? I'm sure you have time."

I glanced at my watch. "Well, I have time for a quick coffee but I mustn't be long. I have a class at half past ten."

It was comforting to come out of the cold into the friendly warmth of the bar and I was glad that I'd bumped into Don Federico as I had several things I wanted to tell him.

"Now, Freddie, I have something to ask you – a favour in fact."

"Anything! You know I do anything for you." He spread out his arms to demonstrate his chivalry.

"Then please arrange for me to have my typing lessons at a different time. You see, I don't want them at the same time as Luis."

"You *don't?*" He raised his eyebrows in surprise.

"No. Definitely not. I don't want to see him any more."

"But you are lovers…"

"No we're not. Not any more."

"Yes, you are lovers but now you have a lovers' – how do you call it? … a lovers' *tiff!*" He pronounced the last word with immense satisfaction, triumphant in his knowledge of the English language.

"Not really, it's just that –"

"Yes, yes," he insisted, warming to his subject, "what was the reason? Jealousy? Is usually jealousy, is it not? You must beware of jealousy. *'It is the green-eyed monster which doth mock the meat it feeds on'* – Othello, Act three, Scene three."

"Yes, Freddie, you have a quote for every situation but never mind the reasons. Will you do this for me?"

Federico shrugged his shoulders, rolling his brown, spaniel eyes above his raised glass. "Okay, Baby. If that is what you want. You know I do anything for you."

ଔ ଞ

As I crossed the main square, I noticed Emilio sheltering under the cloisters. He was huddled in a corner calling out numbers for that day's lottery draw. *"Para hoy! El gordo para hoy!"* Emilio was blind and, as with most others like him, managed to scrape a meagre living by selling lottery tickets in the street. He was thin, toothless and unshaven and he wore a threadbare, torn coat and battered beret. He went about the streets leaning on the shoulders of his son, an emaciated, deathly-pale youth of around fifteen. Despite their wretched existence, the pair exuded cheerfulness and good nature and I regarded them as friends.

"Emilio!" I called. "Save a few tickets for me before you sell the lot!"

His sightless face lit up at the sound of my voice. "*Vaya!* It is the English señorita. How are you, señorita? How are you today?"

"As pretty as ever, Papá," laughed his son who was a cunning master of flattery, "and I think she wants some tickets."

"This time you will be lucky," grinned Emilio, tearing off the tickets for me. "You will see. This time you will win the *gordo*."

"Yes, you've been telling me this for weeks, Emilio, but I'm still waiting for it."

"But today God will grant you good luck. You will see," said the boy confidently. "But where are you going on such a cold day, señorita?"

"Well, this morning I'm on my way to the Captain General's house."

Their mouths fell open. "*Hombre!*" exclaimed the boy, his face darkening, "why do you have to go to such a place?"

"Duty," I replied. "But don't you worry, my business is not with the Captain General – just his daughters."

Emilio groped around in the air until his bony hand came in contact with my sleeve. He grabbed my arm, muttering under his breath. "Be careful, señorita, be careful! Some people go there and never come out."

Having reminded me of this disturbing fact, my friends took their leave and I hurried on realising I was rather late for my class. As I approached the great building it seemed even more forbidding than usual with its armed guards. However, by now they knew who I was and even saluted me as I walked past them, making me feel like a V.I.P. Once inside I knew how to find my way to the special staircase leading to the Captain General's private apartments, and was soon in the presence of his daughters.

As usual, they greeted me with enthusiasm, even affection, for they always looked forward to their English lessons. I couldn't help feeling that there was something missing in the lives of these young women despite their obvious wealth and position. Perhaps their father's rank, importance and notoriety isolated them from the outside world.

We sat down at the round table, surrounded by canaries, and at that moment the sun, unseen for several days, broke through the mist and flooded the room with warmth and light. The birds hopped around in delight, trilling prettily but I noticed that one of the cages was empty.

"Yes," sighed Magdalena, "it is such a pity. I let it out for just a few minutes to exercise its wings and then Papá came in with the cats and – well, it was all over so quickly."

Since there was nothing further to be said on this subject, we turned our attention to the lesson I had prepared for them.

"As it will soon be Christmas," I began, "I think we shall read through chapter ten which will tell you all about the way we celebrate Christmas in England."

The girls read the lesson in their heavy, Spanish accents and then laboriously translated it. After that, we discussed what they had read. They were fascinated to hear of the strange, pagan habits we indulged in during the Festive Season.

"You mean you hang this plant in the house, this mistletoe, and you kiss under it?" marvelled Elisa.

"Yes, probably has its origins in ancient fertility rites."

"*Dios mío!*" They crossed themselves hastily. "How strange! But then," she added by way of explanation, "you are not Catholics, are you?"

I guessed they were probably forming in their minds a picture of the British as a race of primitive, heathen barbarians still retaining the customs of those rough, Nordic tribes from whom we had sprung.

"Anyway, to continue. It is also a tradition to bring a tree into the house. It must be a coniferous tree like a spruce or fir, and then we decorate it with all sorts of things like coloured lights, presents and glass balls."

"Oh!" exclaimed Elisa. "That is a lovely idea. I have heard of that custom but it's not popular here."

119

"No," I mused, feeling a sudden tinge of homesickness, "I think that's one of the things I shall really miss. This is my first Christmas away from my family."

"But here too we have a good time," she assured me. "We have a big party on Christmas Eve and another on New Year's Eve; but I can understand how you will miss all those strange customs if you are used to them."

"Never mind," I said, "my family are sending me a Christmas pudding which I shall cook for my friends here. It will be interesting to see if they like it. Of course, I would love to decorate a tree for them but I haven't seen one in the shops."

A cat, which had been asleep on a nearby chair, suddenly woke up, stretched itself, yawned and jumping down, padded across the room towards the door. Two others miraculously appeared from nowhere and did the same.

"I think Papá is home," said one of the girls. "They always know when he is home."

I gathered up my books. "And I think it's time to end this lesson. Please finish all the exercises for next time. We shall have one more class next week but, after Christmas, I'm away for a fortnight. In the meantime, I'll set you some work to do. Goodbye for now then, and have a really good Christmas!"

"And you," they chanted. "Pity about the Christmas tree!"

Cß &O

The following day I had my typing lesson alone. Don Federico did not ask any more questions, which was a relief, and in fact said very little as he was obviously feeling unwell. He sneezed several times, his face was flushed and he was shivering. As he sat there with hooded eyes, and head buried in the collar of his overcoat with just a red nose protruding, he reminded me of a sick bird of prey.

"Freddie," I said, "you look really ill. Why don't you go home to bed?"

"I am not ill," he croaked indignantly, "I am never ill. Is just that I have this pain in my stomach. It will go when I have a few *chatos*."

"I think you've caught 'flu."

"Nonsense! I am not a friend of *Doña Gripe*. I never have 'flu, never have colds, never have anything like that. I am the most healthy man alive…"

His speech was interrupted by a bout of heavy coughing.

"But you don't seem healthy now so please go home – to please me?"

"You know I usually do anything to please you," he coughed, producing a cigarette from his pocket and licking the paper to seal it. There was a pause while he put the cigarette in his mouth and lit it. "But this time I cannot. I have another class after this."

"Is it? —" I felt the colour drain from my face.

Don Federico nodded solemnly. "Your lover."

"I wish you wouldn't say that," I snapped, getting up from the typewriter table. "And we'll cut short this lesson if you don't mind for both our sakes. It will give you time to drown those germs of yours in alcohol."

He gave a hollow smile. "Is a good idea," he said.

So I left ten minutes early and rushed down the stairs, two at a time, terrified of bumping into Luis and not knowing how I would react if I did. But my fears were unfounded and the only thing I met was a large rat that flew across my path and dived into a hole at the bottom of the stairs.

When I arrived home, Anita ran out of the house to meet me with pink cheeks and sparkling eyes. "You'll never guess what a strange thing happened this morning." She dragged me into the kitchen which was, as usual, full of people all talking at once. It seemed that half the neighbourhood had gathered there including a good number of children who were jumping up and down in excitement. In the centre of all this was Domi brandishing her frying pan. She poked her fork at me accusingly as I walked in.

"There she is! There's the cause of it all. Child, you nearly had us all die of fright this morning." A shriek of laughter went up from the assembled neighbours. Once order was restored she began her strange story.

"Soon after you left this morning the *army* arrived here. Dozens of soldiers all armed to the teeth. They came in a lorry and hammered at the door. *Dios mío!* I thought they had come to take us all away. This is the end of us, I said to myself. What has Teo been up to? Then they said they had come at the express orders of the Captain General. *Madre mía!* We nearly died of fright."

"Imagine that!" interjected Anita. "We couldn't understand what was happening but then they asked for you."

"Yes, you!" Domi pointed her fork at me again. "They said: 'Do you have an English girl staying here?' I said yes, and then they said they had something to deliver here for you and they went to fetch it from the truck – and what do you think it was?"

I shook my head. "I haven't a clue."

"Why, a *tree!*"

"Yes, a tree! A tree!" shrieked the children in chorus jumping up and down again.

"A ridiculous tree," continued Domi, turning her attention to the tortilla in her pan. "It was far too big to bring into the house so I said to leave it in the patio but no, they said they had been ordered by the Captain General to go up the mountain, cut down a tree and make sure it was brought into this house. They must obey orders so that was what they were going to do. They had to chop a bit off the trunk and now it's in the dining room." She flashed her black eyes at me in disapproval and jabbed aggressively at the tortilla.

"Come and see! Come and see!" yelled the children tugging at my clothes.

Sure enough, propped up in a corner of the dining room was a beautiful, bushy fir tree, its branches still crisp with frost, filling the room with its alpine fragrance. Near the top, nestling among the lush green needles, was a white envelope bearing my name. Inside was a Christmas card from the daughters of the Captain General. It read: "Happy Christmas! We hope this will make you feel more at home!"

CHAPTER THIRTEEN

CHRISTMAS EVE

The Christmas pudding, sitting in the larder in a place of honour, was an object of great curiosity to young and old. Its presence in our house had quickly been broadcast over the entire neighbourhood and children brought their school friends round to view it. They ran to the larder, opened the door and pointed to it with a mixture of awe and amusement, giggling and whispering among themselves that this strange thing was an English 'poodeen'. When I made up the jelly it caused even more sensation. I put it in the larder and everyone was amazed at its shape and texture, never having seen anything like it before. The adults regarded it with some suspicion but the children were fascinated, and delighted in prodding it, screaming with delight at its wobbliness.

It was Christmas Eve and preparations for the evening's festivities were in full swing. The streets were thronged with shoppers, and folk from the countryside dressed in brightly-coloured blankets were selling their produce in the market. Women hurried home with plump, live chickens in their shopping baskets and great flocks of turkeys were being driven along the narrow, cobbled streets. The shop windows were crammed with all manner of festive things: enormous, decorated baskets filled with Christmas *turrones* (a kind of nougat made from almonds and honey), and various other goodies; sinister boars' heads, hollowed out and lit up like Jack O'Lanterns, their huge, goggling eyes glowing red, and elaborate crib scenes painstakingly arranged with no detail forgotten, some complete with moving figures and miniature fountains. There were Christmas cards and, to my astonishment, I even came across one solitary but brightly-lit Christmas tree! It seemed the pagan, yuletide symbols of Northern Europe and North America, which so mystified the Captain General's daughters, were gradually creeping into Catholic Spain.

All was hustle and bustle as the people of Burgos prepared for the night's feasting and merry-making and there hung in the air a feeling of excitement and pleasurable anticipation. Of course, there were many for whom not even Christmas Eve could bring much cheer. The poor, who were as poor as in Dickensian England, might still be hungry on Christmas Day; and then there were the politically oppressed. In many homes we knew there would be sad-faced women packing up small parcels of food to be smuggled, after dark, into the great political prison outside Burgos, where their men folk languished. Incredibly, some of these men had been incarcerated there since the Civil War and the reports of what took place behind those forbidding walls, the stories of suffering and torture, made one's blood run cold. One woman told us why her husband had lost the use of his hands. The prisoners were scrubbing the floors one bitterly cold day but their progress was slow as the water was ice-cold and their hands were numb. Angered by this, the guards had punished them by stamping on their hands, crushing them to a pulp under their heavy, hob-nailed boots. Franco's prisons were bursting with political prisoners. They were mostly left-wing sympathisers or Republican ex-combatants but any with the courage to criticise the dictatorship openly might also be classified as 'reds' and were in danger of finding themselves behind bars. The members of Anita's family were known by the authorities to be 'reds' but she had no father, grandfather or uncles to visit in the Burgos prison. They were dead. Nevertheless, it was suspected that a close watch was being kept on the family.

For the past forty-eight hours, our house had become a hive of feverish activity. Food was piling up in the kitchen; different kinds of meat and fish and fruit galore: oranges, huge tangerines, bananas, grapes, pears, apples, pineapples and pomegranates. Then there were giant bottles of *anis* and other liqueurs, wines and boxes of delicious *turrones*. People were also beginning to gather in the house for it seemed that numerous friends and relatives had all come to stay, with or without invitation. I was at a loss to imagine how they could all be accommodated with only four beds in the house! But no one seemed unduly worried and each new guest was welcomed with open arms.

Anita and I spent some time decorating the dining room with paper chains and Christmas cards before turning our attention to the magnificent Tree which now stood upright in a tub looking more impressive than ever. Soon it was sparkling with the glass balls and tinsel my family had thoughtfully sent from England and to these were added a few small gifts we had bought for each other. In all these preparations we were assisted by an army of children with shining faces. They rushed around us bumping into each other in their excitement, their eyes sparkling at the sight of The Tree in all its splendour.

Meanwhile, down in the basement, Teo was trying to light the boiler. Although the house had a central heating system, it was only put into operation on special occasions due to the high running cost. Happily, Christmas Eve was deemed such an occasion and after Teo had succeeded eventually in his task, the house was soon glowing with comfortable, even warmth. Domi was in the kitchen attending, as usual, to her frying pan but, at the same time, finishing off a black blouse she was making for me to wear at the party. She was extremely clever with a needle and could create any garment out of odd scraps of material without a pattern.

While all this was going on, the guests kept arriving. There were aunts, a grandmother and a great uncle, cousins complete with their children, friends who had been invited and long-lost friends who happened to be 'passing through'.

One of the invited relatives was a young girl called Pilar who had come down from Bilbao to be with her husband over Christmas. Manolo, a young man still in his teens, was doing his military service in Burgos. Apparently the young couple had been obliged to get married as Pilar had become pregnant and this had caused a considerable scandal in the family. To add to her misfortunes, the baby, when it arrived, was stillborn. The poor girl was obviously still suffering from the effects of all these traumas for she seemed very tense and her undeniable beauty was marred by a deathly pallor and a drawn, almost haggard look. It was decided that she and her husband should occupy the one precious double bed since they saw so little of each other.

The afternoon was a very busy one for Anita, Aunt Domi and me. As soon as the midday meal was cleared away, we began preparations for the mammoth feast which would have to satisfy so many mouths that night. We spent hours chopping vegetables and preparing meat and fish while Domi swung into top gear with the frying pan, her voice raised in song, competing with the cheerful sizzling sound of her cooking. Teo, perched as best he could on the edge of the table, surrounded by chopped vegetables and fruit, tried to accompany her on his guitar. Great Uncle Jorge sat, toothless and wheezing, contemplating his hands which were gnarled and twisted into arthritic knots. Between bouts of coughing, he chided them bitterly for their uselessness.

Pilar sat in a corner in her dressing gown, her great mass of chestnut hair cascading over her shoulders to her waist. Silent and withdrawn, she was painting her nails a lurid shade of blood red. The resident children ran in and out shouting, laughing and occasionally crying while those from the street still popped in from time to time to make sure all was well with the jelly and the Christmas pudding. Soon, the tiny kitchen became unbearably hot as everyone continued to crowd into it and the blue, smoky haze rising from the pan of olive oil filled the room with its pungent fumes inducing in poor Uncle Jorge a fresh bout of coughing.

During a temporary lull in the noise and congestion, I turned on the radio to see if it were possible to find any foreign stations. To my amazement and delight, I suddenly discerned, between crackles and hissing, a familiar and nostalgic sound, faint at first but, with careful tuning, becoming gradually clearer and louder. It was the unmistakeable and utterly English sound of the choir of King's College, Cambridge performing their annual carol concert. Miraculously, those cherubic voices rendering 'The Holly and The Ivy' had brought into this thoroughly Spanish kitchen all that seemed to epitomize an English Christmas. It reminded me of my family and, for a moment, I drowned in a wave of homesickness, shedding a few tears onto the pimiento I was cutting up. Anita gave me a hug, lent me a hankie and reminded me that there was to be a party, adding mysteriously, that someone called José Luis would be there and he was bound to cheer me up. Although this was the first time I had heard of this individual, she obviously thought that just the prospect of his presence should be enough to revive my spirits.

CB   BO

It was ten thirty in the evening and the long table in the dining room had been set with numerous knives, forks and wine glasses. The famous pudding was now steaming away on top of the stove, watched over by its ever attentive young guardians. Also of interest to them was the large bowl of brandy butter standing nearby. From time to time a surreptitious finger would dive into it followed by noises that seemed to register approval. Manolo had arrived and had disappeared with Pilar into their bedroom. Great Uncle Jorge was dozing in his chair, oblivious to the shrill voices and loud laughter which pervaded the whole house. Teo was playing his guitar and everywhere one looked there was food.

Anita and I had at last escaped to our room to prepare ourselves for the night ahead, a night when nobody would sleep, a night of non-stop merry-making. Anita donned her best grey dress and her new peep-toe shoes. She applied mascara to her lashes, painted her nails, put on her gold, gypsy earrings, smothered herself with a most alluring perfume and placed a fresh carnation among her black curls. The end result was so devastating that I rated my own chances with the much-prized José Luis as negligible with such a rival as this! I told her so as I changed into my new black blouse which Domi had just finished and which fitted me perfectly.

"Nonsense!" she laughed. "I told you he likes blondes. Here – catch!" She tossed another bloom in my direction. "I got one for you too. Wear it in your hair! It will draw attention to it."

Down in the hall, more people were arriving: Pablo, Anita's

elder brother who had just come off duty at the Provincial Hospital, Carmela, the watch-maker, José Mari, her son and her sister Elvira. These were great friends of the family for the sisters once had a brother who was engaged to Domi long ago but, like so many of that generation, he had died in the Civil War. Domi had never forgotten him, never considered marrying anyone else and had remained friendly with his family ever since. Carmela was a widow and, after her husband's early death, had bravely taken over his watch-making business to keep her and her small son. Every day found her working long hours in the dark little shop which huddled in the shadow of the cathedral.

When the last of the supper guests had arrived, we all squeezed round the long table and the feasting began. We had soup followed by two kinds of fish served with green peas, pimientos and asparagus; meat with tomato sauce, boiled chestnuts, fruit salad, jelly for the children (which proved very popular) and, of course, the Christmas pudding. The latter inspired some mistrust. Here was something strange and foreign, rather too spicy and rich, something to be approached with caution; but most of the men seemed to enjoy it and the children demanded second helpings. Great Uncle Jorge was sporting enough to try a small helping of the jelly. After the first tentative spoonful, he poured the contents of his liqueur glass over the remainder, announcing that it was better that way. Of course, the whole meal was washed down with several different wines and ended with coffee, liqueurs and *turrones*.

By the time we finished eating it was one in the morning, Christmas Day already, and I was feeling so bloated with food and stupefied with alcohol that I could barely rise from the table. However, there was no time to sit around and recover as the dishes had to be cleared away and washed and already the guests were beginning to arrive for the party. Anita's family, who were not religious, had not attended Midnight Mass but a good many of the party guests had done so and were now coming straight from church.

Once the meal was cleared away, we moved the radio into the dining room and pushed the long table against the wall. The children were clamouring for their presents and soon The Tree was stripped of its little parcels while, all the time, more and more guests kept arriving. They included our neighbours, Mari, Miguel and their daughters, our friends Marisol, Gonzalo, Sergio, Felipe and Mari Carmen and last but not least, the celebrated José Luis. He certainly lived up to expectations. Tall, slim and dark with an olive complexion and warm, chestnut eyes, he was impeccably dressed and had about him an air of charm, sophistication, and *savoir faire* that seemed quite irresistible.

"*Ay!* José Luis!" cried Anita, taking his coat and hanging it up in the hall. "I'm so glad you could come. Happy Christmas!"

He took her extended hand and raised it to his lips, all the time caressing her with his seductive eyes. "Happy Christmas to *you*," he murmured in a warm, sexy voice, "and mine is all the happier for being in such delightful company. Every time I see you, you are more beautiful – if that is possible!"

Anita giggled. "Thank you, José Luis. Now, there is someone I would like you to meet: an English friend who is staying with us."

He turned his languid eyes in my direction, then stepped forward to kiss my hand, looking me up and down as he did so. I guessed he was an experienced judge of females, the traditional Don Juan type, always on the look out for new conquests. He greeted me with a dazzling smile, revealing a perfect set of gleaming white teeth. "This certainly is my lucky night," he purred.

Anita had slipped away to welcome more guests. The irrepressible Marisol had arrived and swept past breezily, with lovelorn Sergio in her wake. Her excited laughter soared above the animated conversation of the other guests and her smiling face, still aglow from the chilly night air, was the picture of exuberance. She paused to greet me with a great bear hug. "Where did you find that beautiful tree? I've never seen anything like *that* in this house before." Not waiting for a reply, she was away again and disappeared into the throng. From the dining room came the sound of popping corks and music.

"Listen! They are dancing," said the purring voice close to my ear. "Shall we join them?"

José Luis danced smoothly and gracefully. He skilfully avoided the other couples in the crowded room, his remarkably handsome face smiling down at me, his conversation witty and sprinkled with flowery compliments.

"Your hair, it is so beautiful, like gold." He lifted a hand to stroke my mousy locks. "And so soft! It is as soft and fine as the purest silk."

"I see you are highly skilled in the Spanish art of flattery," I suggested.

He looked hurt. "Believe me, this is not flattery, this is the truth. Your hair is beautiful and so is your blouse. Blonde girls look marvellous in black."

Felipe was dancing with Mari Carmen, Anita with Gonzalo and Marisol with Pablo. Teo was tuning his guitar in a corner and Sergio was standing sulkily by the Christmas tree, a glass in one hand and a bottle in the other, watching Marisol. Manolo and Pilar were also dancing but with little enthusiasm. The children had finished unwrapping their presents and now joined the dancers, weaving their way between the adults and, occasionally, tripping them up. Most of the older generation stood around in groups, replenishing their glasses and discussing politics.

So the night wore on and the wine kept flowing freely. The music from the radio had now been replaced by Teo and his guitar, his lusty voice rising above the others who joined him in singing popular songs. For the dancers, sensuous, pulsating Latin American rhythms flowed from his guitar and around three in the morning, when everyone was feeling the effects of the wine, these changed to wild flamenco. Gonzalo cleared himself a space in the middle of the floor, tied the ends of his jacket into a knot to simulate the costume of an Andalusian dancer and started to stamp around, tossing his head and clicking his fingers, his face acquiring a haughty and disdainful expression. Unfortunately, the effect was somewhat marred by the fact that his glasses were wobbling precariously at the end of his nose; then one particularly violent toss of the head sent them flying across the room amid delighted squeals from the younger spectators. Fortunately, they were quickly rescued by Sergio before they could be smashed. Marisol and Miguel now joined in the flamenco dancing while the rest of us clapped rhythmically and the children yelled *"Olé!"* Soon most of the other guests were clicking and stamping with the notable exception of Felipe who was deeply involved in fighting an imaginary bull in the hall. It was very temperamental, he assured us, and nervous and had to be handled with the utmost skill. To this end, he had found Domi's table cloth and had taken up a strategic position by the staircase where he stood, shaking the cloth and making encouraging noises at his invisible opponent. José Mari and several other young males watched him, fascinated, and had to be restrained from rushing in to play the part of the bull.

Meanwhile, in the kitchen, Domi and her friends were packed around the *brasero* playing cards, surrounded by a crowd of interested on-lookers, gossiping, laughing and drinking. Suddenly, this cosy scene was shattered by Manolo reeling across the room, pushing his way to the back door, his hand clamped to his mouth. Domi leapt from the table and rushed to unbolt the door and only just in time as the contents of Manolo's stomach shot out across the patio.

José Luis, who never seemed far away, glided up beside me. He shook his head pityingly as he surveyed the undignified spectacle in the patio. "Dead drunk," he observed. "It's sad to see how some people react after a few drinks. Have you seen that poor fool in the hall?"

José Luis himself was still in complete control of all his faculties despite having drunk the same as the rest of us and, indeed, he remained annoyingly sober for the rest of the night.

Manolo, having relieved himself at both ends, came back into the house. Pilar rushed over to him sobbing but he pushed her roughly aside and stormed out of the kitchen. He crossed the hall, thrusting his way past Felipe who assumed he was the bull and performed an elegant *pase* with the table cloth. Thence he staggered up the stairs to their bedroom and slammed the door noisily. Pilar ran up after him screaming and all the guests gathered in the hall and stood at the foot of the stairs to see what would happen next.

Terrible sounds came from above: something being smashed

against the wall, something being crushed under foot, something being ripped up – all to the accompaniment of Pilar's hysterical shrieks. Next, we heard the bedroom window being flung open. Anita and I rushed out into the patio to see what would come flying out, spreading our arms wide in case it was Pilar. We saw Manolo's figure silhouetted against the light of the window, his arms filled with strange bundles. One by one the various articles came hurtling down through the frosty night: a skirt, a dressing gown, two jumpers and a nightie, closely followed by assorted shoes and torn-up nylons. There was a slight pause during which we feverishly tried to gather everything up, then another missile whistled past us, narrowly missing Anita's head. It landed with a rattle at the far end of the patio and I picked it up. It was a money box, smashed and empty.

Back in the house, a frightening scene confronted us. Manolo and Teo were shouting at each other angrily in the hall while Pilar sobbed uncontrollably in Domi's arms.

"He's taken our savings! All the money that we have saved up together – he's got the lot," she wailed. "And he's smashed my jewellery and thrown all my clothes out of the window."

"Give her the money, *imbécil!*" shouted Teo, barring Manolo's way to the front door.

"Out of the way unless you want your face smashed in!" bellowed Manolo.

"Oh, so that's how you want it!" Teo started to roll up his shirt sleeves. Anita gave a little scream and grabbed her brother by the arm. "No, Teo, Leave him alone! Can't you see he's drunk? He doesn't know what he's doing. Let him go!"

"The bastard's not leaving this house till he's apologised to Pilar and handed over the money."

"Who do you think you are?" shouted Manolo lurching towards Teo with raised fists. Everyone moved back to give the antagonists room to settle the matter but Anita was determined that violence should not prevail. "Don't fight him Teo!" she pleaded. "I don't want you getting hurt."

Teo laughed. "Me hurt? By that worm? You must be joking! I'm going to teach him a lesson he won't forget in a hurry."

At this, Manolo lunged at him like an enraged beast but his aim was poor and the blow missed Teo's face by several inches. The children gasped in delight, – there was more than enough entertainment for them that night – and the women screamed. Pilar drew away from Domi and ran forward to stand between the two men, her small arms stretched out in an attempt to separate them.

"Manolo," she sobbed, "haven't you done enough damage for one night? Just get out of here! Let him go, Teo! It doesn't matter about the money. I just want him to *go*."

Reluctantly, Teo stepped aside. Manolo slunk past him, spitting insults and struggling into his raincoat while somebody opened the front door. The next moment he had vanished into the night to everyone's relief. The uneasy hush that had come over the guests during those last tense moments was now broken and everyone started talking at once. Pilar was still crying but, at the same time, between her tears, she was already making plans to return to Bilbao that same night.

"What's the time? Four o'clock? If I hurry I can catch the five o'clock train. Can you lend me money for the fare, Domi?"

"Nonsense, child! You can't travel in the state you're in. You must get some rest."

"No! no! I want to go home. Please call a taxi! I have to pack my things."

No one could dissuade her from her decision. She ran upstairs and came down moments later clutching her case, her face swollen and red, her uncombed, tangled hair pulled back into an untidy bunch. She looked very small, young and pathetic: a child trying to cope with the problems of a woman. We never found out whether the young couple had quarrelled during the course of the evening and this was the reason for Manolo's outrageous behaviour, or whether it could simply have been attributed to alcohol. Pilar went home to her parents that same night and I never saw her or Manolo again.

With her departure, the party resumed. Guests helped themselves to more drinks and music returned to the dining room. By this time it was nearly five in the morning and some were

133

beginning to flag. Great Uncle Jorge had fallen asleep in his chair in the kitchen and the younger children were taken upstairs and popped into one of the beds. Pablo and several others who had partaken of the Christmas pudding announced they were not feeling well and disappeared discreetly to be sick. I guessed the pudding had been made a convenient scapegoat for their over-consumption of alcohol as I noticed that none of the children suffered such ill effects.

Sergio had finally succeeded in dancing with Marisol, and, for the first time that evening, I saw him looking happy as he gazed down at her adoringly. Gonzalo and Felipe were both trying to dance with Anita at the same time, pushing each other away playfully, Anita's laughter rising above the noisy banter.

Over in the corner, José Luis, still managing to ooze sex appeal even at that hour, was nonchalantly smoking a cigar and chatting up Mari Carmen who stood close to him, spellbound, hanging on his every word.

Out in the hall Domi was saying goodbye to some of the neighbours who had decided to take themselves home to their beds and so, gradually, the party was dispersing. At last there was room to breathe and space to move. I found myself yawning and debated whether or not it might be possible to creep unnoticed up the stairs and surrender myself to blissful slumber. The thought was tempting so I started to edge my way towards the door, in and out of the dancing couples, but my plans were thwarted by Prince Charming who had noticed my retreat. Hastily excusing himself, he left Mari Carmen and came bounding over.

"And where is my enchanting *inglesa* thinking of going? You are surely not leaving us? Come! You have not danced with me for at least half an hour and my heart is breaking!"

He took me firmly by the hand and dragged me back to join the dancers who were now jerking and gyrating to the beat of a rumba. The heady scent of his after shave mixed with the sickly-sweet smell of cigar tobacco, made me feel even drowsier and I was only half aware of what he was saying as we danced. I heard vaguely: "What are you doing tomorrow? We could go dancing. There is a good dance at the Military Sports Centre…"

"Sorry. Anita and I have to get ready for our holiday," I yawned, "and we have a lot to do. We're heading for Andalusia in a few days time."

"Ah! That is good news. To reach Andalusia you have to travel first to Madrid, don't you?"

"Well, yes."

"And I live in Madrid so we could see each other. Does that make you happy?"

I smiled to myself, amused at his conceit. "Deliriously," I replied.

ભ ૪૦

It was morning. Seven thirty in the morning on Christmas Day and most of the guests had departed. Those of us in the house would have to sleep in relays as there were insufficient beds to go round. Great Uncle Jorge had been installed in Teo's room and Teo planned to sleep on the floor.

"One of you girls will have to sleep with José Mari," threatened Domi pointing to Anita, me and Carmela's twelve-year old.

"Well I'm not," said Anita firmly. "I'm not sleeping with him – and that's definite."

"You surely don't expect *me* to, do you?" barked her aunt. "I'm not sleeping with a restless child. I need some sleep." They both looked at me expectantly.

"Alright," I sighed, "I don't mind. Nothing could keep me awake."

So Anita doubled up with Domi and I had no alternative but to share my bed with José Mari. The boy crept in beside me grinning sheepishly and not a little embarrassed; but no sooner had his head touched the pillow than he was out like a light and lay stone-still until four in the afternoon.

"We can sleep until eleven," Domi had announced as she turned out the lights, "and then we must get up and give someone else a turn."

As I nestled down into the sheets and lay, listening to the

heavy breathing coming from the small, unconscious form beside me, I thought what a strange way to spend Christmas Day! I had resolved to banish from my head all thoughts of Luis and what he might have been doing that night. Every time such thoughts tormented me, I had just filled up my glass, deadening the senses a little more. Now, drifting into sleep, I still managed to keep them at bay. But once asleep, our unfettered minds go their own unruly way and that night, when I dreamt, it was not of José Luis.

CHAPTER FOURTEEN

COWBOYS AND A MONSTER

Aunt Domi 's voice, raised in cheerful song, drifted up from the kitchen and roused me into wakefulness. "*Ay Señorita*, I am single and in love!" I recognised the words and tune as a song from a Spanish *zarzuela*, a sort of light opera or musical, popular with her generation.

After all the hectic activity of the days leading up to Christmas, I felt entitled to the odd lie-in for there had been little sleep for any of us lately. First, the dawn rising to listen to the Christmas Lottery results and the accompanying disappointment of not finding ourselves instant millionaires, then all the preparations for Christmas culminating in that eventful Christmas Eve party. We now had before us several days respite before embarking on our adventurous journey down to southern Spain. Just one more party, on New Year's Eve, and then we would be off, so with no classes for a while, it was time to relax. A glorious feeling of space and freedom told me that Anita was already up and I had the bed to myself. Blissfully, I stretched out my limbs and one of my toes came into painful contact with a cold, solid object at the end of the bed. It was the brick that Domi heated for us in the oven every night when the weather was cold. We would wrap it in newspaper and take it to bed where, with luck, its warmth would last for most of the night. The fact that it was now completely cold, reminded me that I was unforgivably late in waking. Now Anita's voice was calling from below.

"Wake up! The post has come."

She ran upstairs and burst into the room clutching a bundle of letters. "There's one from England – your family, I expect – and one for you from Madrid and one for me from Madrid as well."

I pulled myself into an upright position to read the letters. The one from my family was an up-date on all their news and the one from Madrid was from a friend I had made while staying in that city the previous spring. I had been introduced to Rafael at the British Club by an English boy called David, doubtless in the hope that Rafael might relieve him of the irksome task of showing me Madrid. David, who had taken me out a few times when we both lived in London, had now found himself a permanent job in Madrid together with a very attractive Spanish girlfriend. He therefore had little time for boring English girls who wanted to be shown the sights. His plan worked, for Rafael seemed only too ready to step into his shoes and we spent an hilarious week together exploring all the night spots before Julio arrived from Logroño and put an immediate stop to our escapades.

'I'm delighted that you'll soon be visiting Madrid on your way to Andalusia,' read Rafael's letter, 'and that you are bringing a friend, and that the friend you are bringing is pretty. I have already told Desmond Brocklebank about your friend and he is anxious to make up a foursome.' I read this last bit out to Anita who was intrigued.

"Who is this Desmond what's-his-name, and will I like him?"

I laughed. "I very much doubt it! He's the oddest character I've ever met, another member of the British Club and they're all pretty odd there. His name is English but, in fact he's half Spanish. I must warn you, he's about forty, much too old for you, and he's very strange to look at. Also, he has the most extraordinary ideas. In fact, I think he's mad."

Far from being put-off, she seemed even more intrigued. "He sounds interesting," she mused. "He sounds different."

"Yes, he's certainly that. He calls himself an existentialist – whatever that is – and he has a beard and goes around in a duffle coat. No, I don't think you'll like him at all."

"We shall see. I'm looking forward to meeting this strange Englishman. Now, let me tell you about my letter. It's from some good friends of ours, Demetrio and Auri, and they've invited us to stay with them, so that will save us hotel bills while we're in

Madrid. Oh! I'm so excited about our holiday! To think we'll see all those places: Granada... Seville... I can't wait!"

Our reveries were interrupted at that moment by Domi screaming up the stairs that it was high time one of us went out to fetch the milk. I washed and dressed hastily then grabbed a couple of large jugs and set out into the frosty morning for the dairy.

A queue of people holding jugs and bottles had already formed, standing in the newly-fallen snow outside the dairy and stamping their feet. The milk was late that morning, probably because of the bad weather. I noticed Marisol was also waiting so I went over to talk to her.

"I'm glad you gave poor Sergio a dance on Christmas Eve," I said. "You know he's been so miserable lately."

"Sergio?" she repeated distractedly, scanning the distance for signs of the dairyman's approach. "Why? What's the matter with him?"

"As though you didn't know! That poor boy's crazy about you and you're driving him to drink with your indifference."

"*Ay! Que exagerada!*" she exclaimed. "How you exaggerate! That's all nonsense. Your head is full of silly romantic notions. You shouldn't take any notice of what he says. Anyway, let's talk about something more interesting. Are you going to the cinema this afternoon? They're showing a good western with Gregory Peck and he's so handsome."

The sound of trotting hooves and cart wheels grinding in the snow announced the arrival of the dairyman who was full of apologies.

"This weather! It's terrible for beasts. It took such a long time to get them fed and milked this morning and then the roads; impossible! We could hardly get through in some places."

He and his round bustling wife started unloading the heavy churns, carrying them into the little dairy while the mules stood stamping and snorting, their warm breath clouding the frosty air. Soon the wife was behind the counter, ready to serve the first customers, ladling the milk straight from the churns into their containers. The women gossiped and laughed as they waited their turn in the queue while the children played hide and seek round their skirts. Most of the women, particularly the older ones, were dressed in black: black dresses, black cardigans and black shawls draped round their shoulders. Standing in the snow outside the little shop, they looked like a flock of crows. I remembered that it was still customary for widows to wear mourning for life and, after the Civil War, there were plenty of widows.

Having agreed to meet Marisol that afternoon at the cinema, I walked very carefully back to the house carrying the jugs. They were full to the brim and I prayed I would not slip on the ice and spill the lot. I arrived at the same time as the baker on his morning round. He had just delivered our daily order of *vienas*, long greyish-white baguettes, still warm from the oven despite the cold, because the bakery was only just down the road.

Breakfast tasted particularly good that morning: great cups of warm, milky coffee and hunks of crusty bread all enjoyed round the warmth of the *brasero*. This time, we only found one rusty nail in our bread and two hairs – both blonde. The fact that they were blonde, Teo pointed out as he carefully removed his, proved that the baker's wife had been responsible for that morning's baking. Had it been the baker himself, the hairs would have been black, as was frequently the case.

Both the baker and his wife were genial souls and had, on one occasion, obligingly accommodated in their oven an apple pie which I had made as a novel English birthday present for a friend and which would not fit into Domi's small oven. We had formed a strange procession that day, me at the head, bearing the pie followed by Aunt Domi and Anita surrounded by a throng of excited children and the odd curious neighbour. The baker, having examined the pie suspiciously, agreed it could join the latest batch of his *vienas* and, when it later emerged, crisp and golden brown, it was baked to perfection and proved delicious.

Breakfast over, we went about our respective tasks, Domi and Anita to household chores and I to the station to buy the kilometric tickets that would shortly take us on our journey to adventure in the south. Such tickets could be used to travel anywhere in Spain up to a certain number of kilometres and were extremely economical.

These bought, I next hurried to the cinema to get tickets for the afternoon's performance. There was only one cinema and the films shown were usually many years old but nobody cared about that. For an unsophisticated audience without instant visual entertainment at the press of a button, a trip to the cinema was the highlight of their week. Since Aunt Domi loved westerns and Anita was a great fan of Gregory Peck, I was instructed to buy three tickets for 'Duel in The Sun'.

Standing at the top of the steps, outside the cinema, were Sergio and Gonzalo . They were studying a lurid poster depicting Jennifer Jones, semi-clad and bleeding, clawing her way over a dusty ridge towards Gregory Peck, also prostrated and gory. Gonzalo looked round, and at the sight of me, gave a cowboy whoop and raced down the steps, twirling an invisible lasso.

"*Hola*! Looks good, doesn't it?" he said indicating the poster with a toss of his head. "Hurry up and get your tickets, and then come and join us for a drink."

So it was that I found myself in the Espolón, sandwiched between Gonzalo and Sergio among the crowds enjoying a stroll before lunch. The sun was shining brilliantly, casting long, mauve shadows across the glittering snow. The cathedral, with its frosted spires, looked particularly beautiful against a sky of cloudless sapphire. It would have been a perfect stroll had I not, at that moment, spotted among the sea of faces, the one I most dreaded seeing. Gonzalo was still acting the fool in his role as a cowboy, shooting from the hips at the café windows, and Sergio was watching him with amusement. But I was oblivious of their antics, seeing only Luis's tall figure, wearing the familiar wind-cheater with the collar turned up, his head inclined towards a short girl in a black coat who clung to his arm. She was looking up at him adoringly as they chatted together.

Instantly, I was enveloped in a fire of terrible jealousy, completely uncontrollable and frightening in its intensity. It was a basic, primitive passion not experienced since early childhood. It came bubbling up through layers of self-control, built up over the years, to erupt like a volcano, shaking me from head to foot. As predicted by Federico, Shakespeare's 'Green-eyed Monster' had sunk its teeth deep into my neck. How dare this dowdy girl in a black coat take my place! Take what belonged to me!

He's yours, not hers! hissed the Monster in my ear. *Tear her away from him! Go over and confront them both and tell her the truth!*

I suppressed this temptation with difficulty and instead prayed that Luis would not look up and see me and what was written on my face. The next minute they had walked by and disappeared into the crowd.

"Hey! Are you alright?" Gonzalo had caught me by the arm and was peering at me anxiously. "You look like you're..."

I laughed a little hysterically. "It's you, Gonzalo, you're so funny! Whoever saw a cowboy in glasses? You're crazy and you've made me laugh so much I'm almost in tears."

Gonzalo, whose comical face always registered surprise, looked more amazed than ever.

ය ෬

Until now, I had been feeling rather pleased with myself at having succeeded in blocking out thoughts of Luis and generally recovering from the break-up of our relationship. After those first few miserable, sleepless nights, I had come to the conclusion that melancholy brooding was counter-productive and making my situation worse. In order to forget my pain, I had filled every hour with feverish activity, throwing myself whole-heartedly into my teaching, going to dances or the cinema with Anita, meeting friends, and helping Don Federico with his evening English classes. But now, seeing Luis with the girl whose very existence I had refused to acknowledge, was like opening the floodgates and the memories kept pouring in. I recalled those warm, summer days when we had first met at Federico's academy, the joy of being alone with him after lessons, the first time we kissed. I remembered our walks by the riverside at dusk, watching the sunset's reflections in the water; our strolls out into the country, those golden afternoons of autumn, with the leaves fluttering down to land on our faces as we lay under the poplars, making plans for when we would be together in Madrid, just the two of us, away from prying eyes and gossiping tongues. Of course, it was all hopelessly romantic and it couldn't last.

Despite being haunted by these bitter-sweet memories, I was careful to hide my feelings from Anita who had an uncanny insight into what was going on in my mind. She had resolved to cure me of my madness and was quite pleased with my progress so I couldn't disappoint her by confessing to a relapse. She had gone to such pains, even to the extent of inviting José Luis all the way from Madrid to the Christmas Eve party in the belief that his looks and charm might be enough to distract me from thoughts of Luis.

The film was full of blood, passion and unrequited love ending with the two main characters destroying each other slowly, painfully and with a good deal of mess. Aunt Domi enjoyed every minute of it and was in a good mood for the rest of the evening.

Apart from western films, Domi had a passion for reading paperbacks of the same genre. Often, during those long winter evenings, we would all four of us sit round the *brasero*, buried in our books, each of us locked into a separate world. Teo would walk through the olive groves with the gypsies of García Lorca's poems or share the tortured lives of the characters in his plays. Of course, all works by the murdered poet were banned, but Teo kept a horde of them in a secret hiding place in his room. Lorca, in common with many other intellectuals, had been arrested in Granada by the Falangists during the Civil War and executed, along with others, in an olive grove.

Meanwhile, Anita would be far away in nineteenth century Russia, starving in freezing garrets with consumptive idealists, plotting revolution by candlelight, dying in the snow or locked into a world from which there was no escape. These were among the themes of the Russian authors she so admired: works by Dostoevsky, Chekhov, Turgenev and others.

Domi, however, was quite happy to ride with her cowboys, sharing their unending struggle against malevolent Indians. This was her chosen form of escape from the drudgery of everyday life. As for me, I was in the habit of picking up Domi 's discarded paperbacks which were mostly within the limits of my basic Spanish vocabulary. Anita, who clearly disapproved of her aunt's choice of literature, had snatched them away and planted before me a formidable tome entitled 'Dead Souls' by Nikolai Gogol. Reading Gogol in Spanish was no easy matter and that book took me the whole winter to finish.

That evening, after my experience in the Espolón, I didn't feel up to tackling another chapter of 'Dead Souls', so I surreptitiously extracted, from Domi's pile of discards, a paperback bearing the title 'The Ride to White Eagle Creek'. Alas, Anita was quick to notice and pointed to it with disapproval.

"Why are you going back to that rubbish?" she chided. "And why have you got such a long face?"

I shrugged and opened the book defiantly. She came over and put her arms round me. "You don't need to tell me," she said, regretting her abruptness, "but you've no business to feel depressed when we're about to set out on our holiday."

This reminded me of the one really pleasant thing that had happened that day. I pushed the offending book aside and returned her hug. "I went to the station this morning," I said, "and I've bought our kilometric tickets."

CB ⠀ BO

The New Year's Eve celebrations were less dramatic than those of Christmas Eve. There was, of course, a large meal followed by a party and, to amuse the guests, Anita, Teo, Miguel and I performed a short play which we had devised and rehearsed over the last few days. It concerned a poor peasant boy who won the Christmas Lottery and suddenly became rich. Without the luxury of television, we had to improvise our entertainments but this was enormous fun and went down well with everybody.

As the Old Year drew to its close, we performed a ritual which was traditional in Spain. Each of us was given twelve grapes to be consumed, one by one, with each stroke of the midnight clock. Anything remaining in our mouths was then quickly washed down with plenty of wine as we all embraced each other and greeted the New Year.

Anita and I were in bed by two and this time, thankfully, there

144

was no sleeping in relays as none of the guests stayed over night. We lay awake for a while, chatting about our forthcoming adventure and I felt happy and relaxed again. For the moment, the Green Eyed Monster had released its grip and slunk away.

CHAPTER FIFTEEN

MADRID

It was four in the morning and snowing hard.

"Look it's coming! Let's get the cases into the hall!"

I ran over to where Anita stood peering through the bedroom window into the dark, freezing-cold night and saw, through the steadily falling flakes, the dim headlights of the Hotel España's bus bumping and jerking up the road towards us.

Hastily, we grabbed our cases, so carefully packed the night before, and rushed down the stairs. Aunt Domi came out of the kitchen stuffing a couple of extra rolls into our picnic bag just as the bus arrived outside our door.

"They're here!" she cried in her shrill little voice. "And now you're really on your way. Take care of yourselves!"

She kissed us both fondly and wiped her eyes on the corner of her dressing gown. At that moment there was a thunderous knocking at the door and, as Domi opened it, a great gust of icy wind swept into the hall, showering us with snow flakes. The driver stood beaming in the doorway, his beret at a jaunty angle, his red, cheerful face glowing like a beacon. He greeted us in a loud, gritty voice, replaced a dead cigarette between his broken teeth and hoisted our two cases onto his shoulders. We followed him out, picking our way across to where the bus stood, its engine ticking over noisily, its two yellow beams of light dazzling us, catching the huge, ghostly snowflakes as they twirled earthwards.

Having installed our luggage on the roof rack, the driver gallantly assisted us into the bus where we took our places among several other sleepy-looking passengers. Peering through the steamy window, we waved frantically to Domi whose small form could just be distinguished through the storm, standing in the doorway, waving back at us and throwing kisses. Then, with a great jerk, we were off, backing slowly out of our little road into the white wilderness.

I never ceased to marvel at the resilience of these decrepit vehicles. Most public transport in this area was of similar vintage and the shabby old bone-shakers were taxed to their utmost: made to climb tortuous mountain passes, drive over pot-holed roads and battle their way through appalling weather conditions. Nevertheless, though painfully slow, they invariably overcame all these obstacles and would eventually arrive at their destinations, albeit a little late.

So it was that we finally arrived at the station. We were late but it didn't matter because, of course, the train to Madrid was late as well. It always was.

Words cannot adequately describe the intense cold of a January night in Burgos in those small hours, and it was with great relief that we clambered up into the relative warmth of a third class carriage. Our fellow passengers roused themselves to greet us, as was the custom, then fell asleep again – all, that is, except a baby in the corner who wailed irritably at the disturbance. Anita and I huddled together on the wooden, slatted seat, arms entwined and heads together, teeth chattering.

For a while we dozed fitfully, shivering and fidgeting until the grey winter's dawn crept reluctantly over the horizon, spreading its chilly light across the bleak stretches of Castilian wasteland which lay grim and brooding under a blanket of snow.

Inside the carriage, the passengers started to stir and stretch their cramped limbs. Someone unrolled a napkin containing sandwiches and cordially offered them round to the rest of us. No one would have dreamt of accepting. Instead, we responded by wishing their owner a good appetite for which he thanked us before tucking in.

This ritual, I learnt, always had to be observed when eating in the presence of others. Failure to do so would have been considered the height of bad manners.

Presently, the train creaked and puffed its way into a station where it came to a standstill with a jolt that sent us all flying into the arms of the passengers opposite. The baby recommenced its wailing and our friend's sandwiches were scattered about the floor.

"*Venta de Baños*," shouted the stationmaster, announcing the name of the station over the noise of slamming doors. A shabby young man grabbed his bag, flung it over his shoulder and opened the carriage door. He turned to say goodbye and wished us a safe journey before jumping lightly onto the platform where he was impatiently pushed aside by a mountainous woman with a broad grin, red cheeks and two crates of chickens. "*Buenos días!*" she wheezed, laboriously heaving herself up into our carriage and squeezing into a vacant seat.

"*Hay caramelos de cafe con leche,*" yelled a sweet seller who was pacing up and down the platform with his wares. "*Hay agua,*" bellowed a water-seller following close behind, bearing a huge leather container. Their shouts were soon drowned by the stationmaster's bell and we were off again. The baby continued to cry and the chickens fluttered and grumbled inside their baskets. Chickens seemed to be a permanent feature of third class travel on the Spanish railways. This time there was no room for them on the luggage rack so they were placed on the floor, rammed against our legs and adding to our general discomfort.

By early afternoon we were approaching Madrid and the carriage had warmed up considerably due to our combined body heat and several bottles of Rioja which the man with the sandwiches insisted on sharing with his fellow passengers. This had put everyone in a good mood and the atmosphere was friendly and jovial. The plump lady had told us in detail about her daughter's confinements, her husband's sick cow and their various feuds with the neighbours. Her company was so entertaining that we could forgive her chickens for pecking occasionally at our ankles.

The man with the sandwiches was singing Aragonese folk songs in a cracked, tuneless voice and two impoverished students from Valladolid had sworn to us their undying love. Even the baby in the corner had stopped crying and was now sucking eagerly at its mother's breast.

The landscape, too, had improved for at last the desolate

plateau had given way to the pine forests of the Guadarrama mountains. Here the sky was clear and blue and the sun sparkled on the snow. Our carriage became full of warmth, light and bonhomie and it was in this happy manner that we finally arrived at the Capital.

CƷ ᙏ

I was no stranger to Madrid and to return to this beautiful city of pink pavements, statues and fountains, was like greeting a long-lost friend. The familiar, much-loved landmarks flashed past the window of our taxi. Here was the Gran Vía, Madrid's main thoroughfare, full of sparkling shops, theatres, pavement cafés and beautiful women. It had been re-named the Avenida de José Antonio since the Civil War, but nobody called it by that name. Now we were circling the Plaza de la Cibeles with its leaping fountains, just as I had remembered it; and then there was that ridiculously grand post office, magnificent as a palace, standing ostentatiously on the corner.

As we approached the Puerta de Alcalá, Madrid's equivalent of the Arc de Triomphe, I wound down the window so that we could hear the sounds of Madrid: the honk of car horns, the rattling and clanging of its ancient trams, the cries of the newspaper boys. Even the bleakness of winter could do nothing to diminish the vivacity of the place. Anita turned to me, with sparkling eyes. "It's wonderful!" she laughed. "Even better than I had imagined."

CƷ ᙏ

How hungry we were for our first meal in Madrid! Never had a casserole tasted better than the one prepared for us by our kind hosts, Demetrio and his wife, Auri.

Demetrio was a tall, slim man in his early forties with kindly brown eyes, a gentle smile and dark hair receding slightly at the temples. His wife was much the same age, short with a round, pretty face and dark curls. They had an adorable pair of identical twin girls, as pretty as dolls, aged about eighteen months. The little

149

family lived at the top of a soulless block of flats in a depressing suburb. The lift never worked and it was a long walk for Auri and her toddlers from the street up to the tiny flat on the sixth floor. Nevertheless, they were thankful to be together in a home at all, for theirs was a strange story.

It seemed the couple had met and fallen in love many years before when they were both young and had planned to marry as soon as they were able. Then came the Civil War and Demetrio had sided with the Republicans. He was captured and thrown into prison as a dangerous leftist, and there he remained for fifteen years. During all this time Auri remained faithful to her fiancé never showing interest in anyone else. She wrote to him and visited him whenever she could and they would comfort each other with the promise that one day, when he was released, they would marry. Auri waited and waited for her love, watching her child-bearing years slip by until at last their dream came true. Parted for all that time, they had never faltered but now they were together and their happiness seemed all the greater for the waiting.

Demetrio was a man of great culture and intellect. Because of his past, he had to take a menial job quite unsuited to his ability and talents but he didn't care so long as he could earn sufficient to keep his wife and children. He found mental stimulation by taking a keen interest in the arts and so the following day, he took us to every museum and gallery in Madrid, culminating in a visit to the famous Prado.

He introduced us to the terrifying 'Caprichos' of Goya, painted during the artist's last years of madness. They depicted a nightmare world inhabited by witches, monsters, devils and beasts. There was a satanic giant crushing the headless body of a man between his claws, the eyes bulging with crazed passion, the great jaws gnawing at the bleeding stump of his victim's arm.

"Satan devouring one of his sons," explained Demetrio. "So do men seek to destroy each other – even those of the same blood." He sighed deeply. It was a relief to move on to Goya's less disturbing masterpieces – his frolicking peasants and voluptuous 'majas'. But then we paused to view a painting with the title 'The Third of May' and were again confronted by the dark side of human nature. This painting showed a bare hill outside Madrid at night where a French firing squad was busy massacring defenceless civilians. One of the victims, kneeling in a pool of blood beside his fallen compatriots, had his arms raised in a last gesture of defiance as he faced his ruthless executioners.

Demetrio shook his head sadly. "I have seen such scenes. Here, in Madrid, I have seen this happen. The only difference was that this time we were murdering our own people."

Anita shuddered. "I've had enough of Goya," she said. "Let's see if we can find Velazquez's '*Infantas*'."

ζ ω

Anita wanted to ring José Luis but I was anxious to look up my old friend Rafael, so in the end it was decided that I would phone him instead.

"So you're here already!" said his delighted voice. "Have you brought that gorgeous friend of yours from Burgos? – You have? Great! Desmond will be pleased. Let's meet up tonight in the Puerta del Sol."

Although there was no snow in Madrid, it was still extremely cold. An icy wind from the sierra whipped round our ankles as we clutched at our coats, pulling up our collars to shield our ears. Why, we asked ourselves, had we not arranged to meet in some convenient, warm café instead of having to stand out here by the entrance to the underground station?

We watched the trams coming and going but there was no sign of our friends. They were late and we were annoyed. Then I felt someone touch my shoulder and I spun round to see Rafael's smiling face, good-looking as ever with those friendly eyes and neat little moustache. He was as dapper tonight as I had always known him, wearing an oatmeal tweed coat, well-pressed trousers and highly-polished shoes. Despite the high wind, not a single hair of his shiny, dark head was out of place.

"Sorry we're late – blame the bus! You should know by now what our transport system is like! Oh! It's good to see you again."

We gave each other a hug. "And it's good to see *you* – even if you have kept us freezing out here for twenty minutes! And Desmond, too – so pleased you could come."

This last remark was not strictly true as I always felt a bit uncomfortable in the presence of Desmond Brocklebank. There he stood, beside Rafael, and what a contrast they made! He was as tall and lean as the figures in El Greco's paintings, with a gaunt, bearded face, thinning hair and large, melancholy eyes. As usual, he was shabbily dressed in an ancient duffle coat with one toggle missing.

"A considerable time has elapsed," he said in his stiff, pedantic English, "since we last had the pleasure of your company here in Madrid. This is indeed a happy occasion." He spoke with a strange, indefinable accent. It could not exactly be described as 'foreign' yet it was unlike native English. I introduced my friends to Anita who treated them to her dazzling smile, her lively eyes assessing each in turn.

"I see your friend is as beautiful as we had been led to believe," said Rafael, well pleased. Desmond took her hand and raised it slowly to his lips, his eyes never leaving her face. "Anita," he murmured. "What a vision is this I see before me?" His Spanish was as clipped and pedantic as his English. He turned briefly to me. "I must congratulate you on your impeccable taste in friends. This is a jewel, nay, a Madonna that my eyes behold."

"Why don't we all go somewhere cosy like the Caves of Luis Candelas?" I suggested. "Their raisin wine is something else! Guaranteed to banish the cold."

We fought our way through the crowds of people in the Puerta del Sol and made towards the old centre of the city. Rafael linked his arm through mine and questioned me about my life in Burgos as we walked along. Why did I have to live there of all places? Such a wild, desolate part of the country with a terrible climate; and those old Castilian houses, so cold and draughty. Why didn't I move down to Madrid and lead a more civilized life?

Ahead of us walked Anita and Desmond. She was chatting away to him, her hands fluttering expressively as she spoke. He, towering above her, still had his eyes fixed on her upturned face.

"Changing the subject," I said to Rafael, "don't you think those two are getting on rather well?"

We reached the wide, cloistered Plaza Mayor. This was an ancient and, to me, rather sinister place since I had read that in this square hundreds of people had been tried by the Inquisition and burnt to death on the spot. Something of their suffering must have lingered in the atmosphere for I could never walk there without feeling slightly uneasy.

Just off the Plaza Mayor were the Cuevas de Luis Candelas. These consisted of a network of caves once used by smugglers but now turned into a remarkable tavern. We dived down and threaded our way from cave to cave until we found a vacant table. Here it was warm and dimly lit, the walls covered with bullfighting posters and all manner of interesting objects and the waiters were exotically dressed as seventeenth century smugglers.

We ordered a large jug of their raisin wine which was made on the premises to a secret recipe. It was delicious and potent and went down very well with a dish of steaming prawns. Across the heavy, wooden table, Desmond and Anita were engrossed in each other's company, oblivious of the world around them. Desmond was expounding some obscure, philosophical theory while Anita gazed at him entranced, listening with rapt attention.

"Personally, I favour Kierkegaard's conception of Man as an isolated individual solely dependent on God rather than the more cynical attitude to humanity expressed by Heidegger." Desmond poured himself another glass of wine. "To me, this is the essence of existentialism."

"What on earth's he talking about?" asked Rafael in a low voice. "He'll bore the poor girl to death!"

Desmond, who had overheard this comment, raised his head and glanced scornfully at his friend. "The trouble is," he said, "the sad fact of life is that the world is populated by the unintelligent. Most of those we see around us have puny minds incapable of any profound thought. There are but few," here he turned to Anita, "who are fortunate enough to be endowed with adequate mental powers."

Rafael gulped and peeled himself another prawn, glancing at me sideways with a cheeky grin.

"You really believe that?" Anita seemed fascinated.

"Indeed I do. Moreover," Desmond leaned across the table, picked up a prawn and pointed it at us. "Moreover, the world is likewise *governed* by the unintelligent. It is for this reason that our lives lie in ruins. *This* is the undoing of the human race." He peeled the prawn and placed it carefully into his mouth as he leaned back in his chair, scrutinizing the ceiling. "Now, if the rulers of the world were hand-picked for their exceptional intelligence, what a different state of affairs would exist! All would be harmony and order, the lower orders surrendering themselves to government by their mental superiors. I have a plan." He leaned forward, his eyes glinting as he warmed to his subject. "I have a plan that could change the world."

Anita put her hand on his sleeve. "Tell us!" she urged. "Tell us about it. It sounds fascinating."

Rafael and I sighed and looked at our watches. We had heard about The Plan before.

"You know, I have formed a society here in Madrid of mentally gifted people – such as myself – rather on the lines of the British MENSA but superior in many ways, our aim being to influence those bodies responsible for the administration of government and, eventually, to supersede them in their duties. We hope to form similar elite groups in all other countries, our ultimate goal being world government. Of course..."

"I think you'll have a job taking over from Franco," I interrupted, laughingly, in English.

He fixed me with a steely stare. "Nothing is impossible for the mentally gifted," he retorted. "Problems are a challenge to be solved by careful logic."

"Oh! What original thinking!" exclaimed Anita, her face glowing with admiration. "How clever you are Desmond!"

He turned his bearded face towards her, regarding her with something close to devotion.

"Sweet goddess, not only am I overwhelmed by your unparalleled beauty, but even more am I astounded by your keen, discerning mind. To find both beauty and wisdom in an individual is rare indeed. You are perfection in womanhood."

As the evening wore on I could see from Anita's glazed

expression, that Desmond had cast a strange spell over her so I decided the time had come to leave.

"We must go," I said firmly, standing up, "Auri will be expecting us back for supper. Tomorrow we have a busy day and in the evening we are leaving for Granada."

Desmond raised his head quickly and his face fell. "Leaving so soon? But you have only just arrived."

"Yes, I know, but we want to visit lots of places and our time is limited. We…"

"Granada," mused Desmond, interrupting me, "one-time seat of Islamic culture, swathed in Eastern mystery. A bewitching city, a place fit even for a goddess."

Anita blushed and patted her curls, smiling happily. Desmond bent his head close to hers and whispered something in her ear to which she responded with a tinkling laugh. The sooner we get to Granada, I thought, the better.

"It is a pity you have to go so soon," said Rafael. "But on the way back you must stop a couple more days in Madrid and we'll get together again."

Desmond and Anita didn't hear him. They were still gazing into each other's eyes, engrossed in muffled, secret conversation.

൭ ൠ

Back in the flat, the twins were running around, late though it was, while Auri was putting the finishing touches to a delicious looking *paella*. "Five minutes!" she called from the kitchen. "Help yourselves to a glass of sherry."

"We can't," said Anita. "Our heads are spinning as it is. They took us to the Cuevas de Luis Candelas."

"Well, no wonder!" said the voice from the kitchen. "Their wine has quite a reputation."

I sank into a chair and at once the twins trotted up and clambered onto my lap, snuggling into my arms like two sleepy kittens. They lay sucking their thumbs and thoughtfully fingering my necklace.

Anita seemed restless and distracted. She wandered around the room sighing and smiling to herself.

"What an amazing person Desmond is!" she murmured. "Are all Englishmen as clever as that?"

"He's only half English," I reminded her defensively.

"But he's so intelligent and so *romantic*! Did you hear what he called me? Madonna! Goddess! Perfection in Womanhood!"

"That proves he's more Spanish than English. Englishmen never say stupid things like that. They're much too down to earth."

Anita wasn't listening to me. She was in a world of her own. "He's very knowledgeable: an expert on Greek mythology and his philosophical ideas are fascinating."

I didn't dare confess to her that I considered him a bore with all the makings of a megalomaniac. Instead I just said: "He's eccentric and he has a very high opinion of himself. Anyway," I added, kissing the two curly heads nestling against my shoulders, "tomorrow we're off to Granada so you had better put him out of your mind."

"Oh! but I don't have to!" she exclaimed joyfully. "I forgot to tell you. He's coming with us."

CHAPTER SIXTEEN

THE ENCHANTED CITY

The following morning I was still reeling from the shock of learning that Desmond Brocklebank was to accompany us to Granada, and even more disturbing, I was now painfully aware that Anita was once again in love. The Spaniards had an expression to describe those who fall hopelessly in love: they were said to be 'like a goat' or 'as mad as goats' and, sadly this was now true of Anita. She went around in a sort of dream, not hearing what I was saying, a foolish smile playing about her lips.

The prospect of having to endure Desmond's company for seventeen hours on the slow train to Granada was daunting enough in itself without having to cope also with a friend who was as mad as a goat. What could be done? Throughout the day I nurtured the faint hope that perhaps the whole thing was wishful thinking on her part and, with a bit of luck, he might not turn up after all. Surely his job must keep him in Madrid?

Alas, all such hopes were dashed as soon as we arrived at the Atocha station that evening for there he stood waiting for us on the platform, long face, beard, duffle coat and all. He was munching an apple and over his shoulders he carried a grubby rucksack.

"Look!" cried Anita excitedly, "There he is! I told you so. I knew he would keep his promise. Oh! How lovely of him to take time off from work just to be with us in Granada!"

Desmond caught sight of us and hurried over but with eyes only for Anita.

"Beauteous Aphrodite," he sighed, "to your other countless virtues must be added that of punctuality." He looked at his watch.

"We have in hand precisely fifteen minutes and thirty seconds before the train is due to depart, ample time in which to seek commodious places for ourselves."

I pointed out that there was no such thing as a commodious place on third class Spanish trains. "We have a particularly long journey ahead," I reminded him. "In fact, I believe we don't arrive until tomorrow afternoon. Are you sure you really want to come?"

Desmond turned to me with a look of mixed pity and disdain. "I am always sure of everything I do," he replied loftily. "Moreover, there is not the slightest doubt in my mind that Fate has had a hand in this matter. Man is not master of his own destiny though he may think otherwise. It is pre-ordained that our paths should meet," he turned to Anita, "and must, from henceforth, be inextricably inter-woven."

As anticipated, the journey to Granada was long, tedious and uncomfortable. To begin with we had the carriage to ourselves and were able to stretch our legs but, as the mail train stopped at every small station, it gradually filled up and we became more and more cramped, making sleep impossible. Beside me, Desmond and Anita were once again deep in philosophical discussion. Opposite sat a priest, his robes dusty and grey with travel. He pored over a small, black book, his lips moving silently and continuously, occasionally bursting out loud into Latin prayer, making everyone jump. Eventually, he too became tired, the light was turned out and we settled down to face the long, cold hours that lay between us and our destination.

Anita shivered and Desmond removed his duffle coat and draped it over her. The night wore on and the passengers shifted around uneasily on their hard seats, coughing, sighing and muttering under their breath. One or two fortunate souls did manage to lose consciousness but their noisy snores made sure that the rest of us were unable to do likewise.

The night seemed interminable but at last the new day arrived, bringing life back to some of those around me. Someone lit a cigarette and the priest yawned and pulled up one of the blinds to admit a stream of dawn sunshine. It felt surprisingly warm. I looked at Anita and Desmond and saw that they were both asleep now, she still curled up under his coat, her head propped against his shoulder.

I looked out of the window and saw, gliding past, a seemingly endless landscape of olive groves planted in neat rows, their silvery foliage contrasting pleasantly with the ochre soil. Beyond, the jagged peaks of distant violet mountains described a curious pattern on the horizon. As the sun strengthened, so did the colour of the sky, deepening to a brilliant sapphire as we passed small villages with pink-tiled roofs and dazzling white walls. Women were beginning to gather with their jugs by the fountains, laughing and gossiping in the sunshine. Others were kneeling by the river with their washboards, sleeves rolled up, scrubbing away at the day's laundry. A very far scene, I thought, from the icy wastes of Castile!

We stopped frequently to unload the morning's mail and exchange passengers. In climbed the country folk with their inevitable chickens but I noticed that these Andalusians were less sociable and talkative than their Castilian counterparts. They sat silent and pensive, staring out of the window with black, inscrutable eyes.

Thoughts of Luis started to creep into my head as we chugged along. What was he doing now back there in Burgos? Was he with his girl? I banished them angrily from my mind. What did I care? Think about something else! I was on holiday and I wasn't going to torment myself any more. I closed my eyes and drifted into a brief, shallow sleep.

When I woke up I found Anita and Desmond awake and chatting. We all three moved out into the corridor to stretch our legs. Desmond opened a window saying that he must flood the lungs with God's fresh, health-giving air, but we were immediately enveloped in a cloud of gritty steam. He closed it again hastily and we looked at each other and laughed.

Here in the south, by mid-afternoon it seemed that even this early in the year, the sun's rays beating through the windows had considerable strength. We were soon sweating uncomfortably in our thick, winter woollies.

Suddenly, one of the passengers – a sullen, unshaven

individual who had sat motionless in the corner for the last three hours, attracted our attention. He pointed towards the window with his cigarette. *"Sierra Neva'a,"* he muttered in a thick Andalusian accent. We looked and were rewarded with a truly fabulous sight. Before us stretched a range of shimmering, white mountains, their snowy peaks glittering against the dark blue sky: fairy tale, sugar-icing mountains, too beautiful, I thought, to be real. This feeling of unreality was to remain with me for the next few days for without doubt, Granada would be the most beautiful place I had ever seen.

CS BO

When we arrived, the city was basking in the warmth and light of a golden, spring-like afternoon. We wandered, as in a dream, through the streets of white-washed houses, their balconies ablaze with geraniums. Behind ornate wrought-iron gates we glimpsed cool patios, mysterious and alluring with their blue and yellow tiles, little fountains splashing among shrubs and flowering plants in terracotta pots. Seeing the palms waving gently against the clear sky, the sun sparkling on the blue-green waters of the river and hearing the birds singing among blossoming almond trees, it was hard to believe that only a few days ago we had left Burgos in a snow storm! The memory of that bitter cold now seemed nothing more than a bad dream.

We found a modest *pensión* down a cobbled back street and were thankful to wash and change our clothes. The proprietress produced a meal of garlic soup, tortillas, fruit and red wine and having thus refreshed ourselves, we set out to explore our surroundings.

Above the city, the Moorish Palace of the Alhambra glowed golden-red in the evening sun; crowning a wooded hill, it stood proud and magnificent against the white *sierra*. Drawn towards this magical place, we started to climb the steep path that led us upwards through aromatic trees and shrubs, pausing from time to time to look back at the white city below. Anita and Desmond walked a little ahead of me still discussing philosophy. How can they keep it up? I wondered. Fragments of their conversation drifted back to me, as I wandered along, enjoying the sweet sounds and scents of the still evening.

"According to Kierkegaard," droned his voice, "the fundamental search for meaningful existence may not lie with science or reason…"

It was dusk when we reached the Alhambra. We walked through the Moorish gateway on either side of which clustered orange trees, their golden fruit glowing warmly among the shiny dark leaves, and found ourselves in a small garden full of whispering palms and cypresses. From a low stone wall we were able to survey the whole of Granada spread out beneath us, bathed in the rich pink of the setting sun and twinkling with myriad tiny lights. We could also see the other famous hill, the Albaicín, home to gypsies and cave-dwellers, sprinkled with countless pinpoints of light like a galaxy of stars that had fallen to earth. From somewhere, far away, the faint strains of someone singing could just be heard drifting upwards over the still air. Anita sighed with pleasure. "This is the loveliest view I have ever seen. I am so happy!" she said.

A wrought-iron gate barred our entrance to the Palace for it was long past closing time. Reluctantly we turned back and retraced our steps, promising ourselves that the following morning would find us back here bright and early.

Now that the sun had set, the temperature dropped dramatically and we shivered in the evening chill. We trotted to warm ourselves up and were soon back in the town walking through dark, narrow streets lit by small lanterns. They shed pools of light against the white walls where trailing plants from the balconies above cast their feathery shadows. Occasionally, we heard the twang of a guitar and snatches of wild, melancholy flamenco. The strange sounds rose and fell, mingling eerily with the approaching night. We walked back to our *pensión* in silence and even Desmond had stopped talking for once. We were all three captivated by the atmosphere of the place as though the city had cast a spell upon us.

CB   BO

"How can the eye take in so much beauty all at once?" exclaimed Anita, radiant with delight. "It's just too much!"

"It's not so much what the eye sees," retorted Desmond in ponderous tones, "as how the brain interprets that which is seen. Something which might appear beautiful to an enlightened individual could pass totally unobserved by the less discerning."

"You mean – beauty is in the eye of the beholder?" I ventured in English.

He ignored me. We were standing among the slender pillars and splashing fountains of the Alhambra, gazing up in wonder at the exquisite Islamic patterns adorning the horseshoe arches around the Court of Lions. I tried to switch off Desmond's lectures and immerse myself in my own reflections.

It seemed to me that the Moorish kings of Granada had, in building their fortress palace at the foot of these snowy mountains, tried to create a private paradise which could delight all the senses simultaneously. The inner palace was composed of a labyrinth of lofty halls and shady courtyards, their graceful arches reflected in pools of turquoise water. Here and there, we came across secluded, leafy gardens which must have provided a blissful refuge from the burning heat of an Andalusian summer. The windows of the Alhambra were like frames surrounding carefully composed pictures of extraordinary beauty. They showed us views of the city and the *sierra* with its wooded foothills glimpsed through sprays of flowering almond. Orange trees spread their branches up to touch the arched windows like a maiden's gentle arms. The beauty of the Moorish carvings was of a fragile, almost ethereal nature. Nothing here was heavy or ostentatious, just a delicate tracery of design flowing over everything: arches, walls, pillars and ceilings. The air was filled with the fragrance of myrtles, cypresses and eucalyptus accompanied by the sound of tinkling water and rustling leaves. This was indeed a world apart: a sensual and exotic world haunted by the ghosts of Eastern princes and their hidden women, a world inadequately described in my guide book. Among the abstract patterns, an inscription in Arabic, beautiful in itself, reminded us that here, in stern and Catholic Spain 'There is no God but Allah'.

Suddenly I became aware that my steps had wandered with

my thoughts and I had lost Desmond and Anita. The last time I had seen them, Anita had been sitting at the Mirador de Daraxa, the loveliest of all the Palace windows. She was looking out over the cypresses while Desmond was trying to take her photograph with an ancient box camera. I hurried to the spot, but they were nowhere to be seen so I walked back to the Court of Lions and stood for a while looking up at the cloudless sky, enjoying the sun on my face. Perhaps they wanted to be alone together I mused drowsily. Certainly they were very much wrapped up in each other and, as the old adage goes: 'two's company, three's a crowd'.

I sighed and wandered back to the seductive little garden I had discovered earlier. Walking round it, I tried to imagine the perfumed women of the harem, flitting like butterflies among the orange trees or sitting by the pool gazing at their reflected beauty in the crystal waters. I peered up through the leaves, seeking out the round, bright oranges. How lovely they looked against the blue sky! It was still a novelty for me to see them growing and more than once I was tempted to reach out and pluck one from its branch.

Just then, I heard the sound of voices and spied the lovebirds themselves standing together under a palm tree, two figures dappled with shade, arms entwined, rapturously gazing into each other's eyes. I resolved that, from then on, I would be discreet and explore the rest of Granada on my own. Quietly, and unnoticed, I slipped away.

CB ꝏ

"*Señorita*, may I join you?"

I was sitting at a pavement café enjoying a refreshing glass of beer and being thoroughly lazy. The sun was quite hot and it was so pleasant just to sit and watch the world go by. It was also a relief not to have to listen to Desmond droning away and I was quite enjoying being on my own for a change. It occurred to me that I had not been left to my own company for many weeks and it was something of a luxury. But alas, it was very difficult in Spain to be alone for any length of time and I realised that this latest intrusion on my solitude was inevitable.

I looked up and saw a smiling young man in a blue shirt. Without waiting for a reply he seated himself at my table and clapped his hands at a passing waiter.

"Another beer for the *señorita* – and a glass of wine." he ordered. He leaned back in his chair, tilting it slightly, and lit a cigarette, regarding me with a pair of eyes black as olives.

"You must excuse me," he smiled, "I can't resist blondes. Anyway, what's a girl like you doing sitting all by herself?"

"Enjoying doing just that!" I replied crossly. "Enjoying my own company and, with your permission, I should like to continue to do so."

Unabashed, my unwanted companion gave a hoot of laughter. "What strange ideas you foreigners have! But here in Spain, girls shouldn't sit alone in cafés so here I am to keep you company. By the way my name is Juan. What's yours and where do you come from? You are foreign, aren't you?"

"English."

Juan shook his head firmly. "Don't pull my leg! You're French."

"English," I repeated wearily, irritated by him already.

"No, you can't be English. I've seen loads of English girls here in Granada and they're not like you. All as plain as mud and dowdily dressed. You're different. Your clothes look – Spanish."

"They are," I replied with a yawn, wishing he would go away. "I live here."

"Really?" Juan leaned forward and studied me with even greater interest. "Where abouts?"

"Burgos"

"Jolín!" he spluttered, rolling his eyes heavenwards in horror. "What a place to choose!" He shuddered at the very thought. "So dreary up there, so bleak and so *cold!*"

"Yes," I agreed reluctantly, "maybe it is, but I like it. The people are great and I enjoy living there."

Juan shook his head sadly at my folly. "*This* is the place to live," he said, holding his glass of wine up to the sun and squinting at it sideways. "Best place in the world."

At this point I had to confess that I had fallen in love with his city and, before long, we were discussing the charms of the Alhambra.

"How about the Albaicín?" he asked suddenly. "Have you been there?"

"Not yet."

"You can't leave Granada without seeing the Albaicín. It's where the gypsies live and if you go there at night they'll sing and dance for you in their caves. That's called a *zambra* – the best flamenco in the whole of Spain. But you can't possibly go there on your own. You'll need an escort: someone who knows the place, preferably a native of Granada, – preferably *me?*"

He was looking at me with his head on one side and with such a quizzical expression that I couldn't help laughing. I studied him properly for the first time and found his dark, gypsy looks quite attractive. By now I was more or less resigned to Juan's company so I said: "Alright. You've persuaded me. We'll go together."

Juan laughed happily at his success. "Most un-English of all possible English girls," he said in his lisping Andalusian accent, "you'll not regret it. Now, let's see, how long are you here in Granada? I would take you this very night but alas! I have to work late today. How about tomorrow?"

"Tomorrow's fine," I said. "The day after we have to leave and I can't think of a better way to spend my last night here."

"*Bueno! bueno!* That's settled then. Nothing warms up there before midnight so I'll pick you up at around nine thirty and we'll have something to eat first. Where are you staying?"

I explained that I was paying full board at my *pensión* so I wouldn't need a meal. "We could meet at eleven thirty," I suggested, "and don't bother to call for me. I'll meet you here at this café."

Juan shrugged his shoulders. "As you please. And now, we just have time for a short walk by the river before I go back to work."

We walked and talked for another half hour and then he left me.

I made my way back to the *pensión* and there were Anita and Desmond. Anita rushed over to me, her face registering agitation and relief. "Where have you been? We've been looking for you everywhere. I was so worried."

"Don't be silly," I said, "I was just exploring the town – having a look at the shops."

"My dear Anita," said Desmond in condescending tones, "I see you do not understand the British. The female of the species is of a tough and independent nature, accustomed to being left to her own devices, unlike the Spanish woman who, like a delicate and fragile bloom, must needs be tended, nurtured and cherished: guarded and protected against hostile forces; treated with the utmost care and vigilance. By contrast, the English woman is like a hardy weed, well able to withstand the rigours of the outside world without suffering any ill effect."

"Thank you, dear Desmond," I said between gritted teeth. "So now we are hardy weeds! That's the second disparaging remark I've heard about us poor English girls today and I'm getting a bit fed up with it."

"Don't take any notice of him!" laughed Anita. "Now listen! Tomorrow we are going to do something very exciting. Desmond and I met some medical students and they've invited us to the hospital to watch an operation – removal of gall stones, won't that be interesting? They said you could come too."

"Er, no thank you," I replied quickly. "I'm sure with your medical background you'll be fascinated but it's not really my scene. Anyway, I've made my own plans for tomorrow. I'm going to visit the Generalife."

"You see what I mean about English women?" commented Desmond with satisfaction.

 C8　80

The following morning found me exploring, on my own, the delightful gardens of the Generalife, summer residence of those incredibly aesthetic Moorish kings. The sun was shining brightly again and the sky was its usual cloudless blue. On either side of a long channel of water leading up to the Summer Palace, rows of fountains threw their sparkling arcs into the air, criss-crossing to form silvery patterns of spray. Paths of pebbled mosaic wandered between cypress hedges and beds of rose bushes already in bloom.

Everywhere there was the sound of lightly splashing water lulling one into feelings of well-being and tranquillity.

I stopped by a little wall crowned with colourful flowers in pots feasting my eyes once more on the fruiting orange trees and listening to the twittering of birds. Beneath me lay the city of Granada and beside it rose the Albaicín. It was good to be alone again for a little while and I rejoiced at the thought that I was here rather than in an operating theatre having to witness the unpleasant spectacle of a surgeon groping around inside someone's exposed digestive organs.

There were few visitors in the gardens that morning and I was able to sun myself in peace and collect my thoughts. What did the future hold for me? Would I stay in Spain or go back to England? My family was pressing me to go home – yet I was having a good time here. On the other hand, I knew I could not stay indefinitely with Anita's family, that wouldn't be fair on them, but neither would I be moving to Madrid now that I had broken with Luis. Again I dragged Luis out of that dark, painful corner of my mind where I had shut him away for the last few weeks. But now I was surprised to find that I could think about him objectively, even calmly. I told myself that it was a good thing that I was free of him for surely a fire that burns so fiercely must die out as quickly leaving behind only ashes. No, better a slow, steady flame. And how about Julio? Dear Julio who, in his conceit, never doubted for a moment my affection for him. I had treated him badly but luckily he didn't know it so, perhaps, when I was back in Burgos, I might make it up to him by spending a weekend in Logroño. After all, if it hadn't been for Julio I wouldn't have ended up in Burgos in the first place.

At that moment, my thoughts were interrupted by the crunch of approaching footsteps on the pebble path and the unexpected tones of my native tongue. I looked round and saw a plump, elderly man. He was quite short and wore a wide-brimmed hat, pale grey suit, colourful tie and rimless spectacles. I sensed at once that he was not English. He was smoking a cigar and looking about him appreciatively, pausing occasionally to consult a small booklet. Round his neck hung an expensive-looking camera and, by his side, trotted an unshaven little man in a shabby uniform who was trying to explain in broken English that here, on this very spot, had stood the American writer, Washington Irving, gathering material for his famous 'Tales of the Alhambra'.

When they reached my wall, the plump man gave me a friendly smile and raised his hat politely. "Buenos deeas!" he beamed.

"Hello," I replied whereupon he removed the cigar from his mouth and walked over to me.

"Well, I mighta guessed you were American too!" he exclaimed. "What d'ya think of this Generaleef? Real pretty, huh?"

"Yes, it's lovely – and this view is fabulous."

"Say! You're English!" he grinned. "I guess you must be with that quaint accent."

I smiled and nodded and he held out his hand to me. "Well, I sure am pleased to meet you," he said, shaking my hand warmly. "Schwartz is the name. Jerry Schwartz. Now, why don't you take a look round this place with me? Meet my guide, José. He's a smart guy and I've been hearing some interesting things about this Generaleef." He patted José benevolently on the shoulder and the little man grinned happily looking like a dog being praised by its master.

So I joined them sensing that Mr. Schwartz was someone used to having his wishes obeyed. Together we strolled through the tree-lined avenues listening to José's painful English. Mr. Schwartz paid great attention to this incomprehensible commentary, nodding his head encouragingly. From time to time the guide would find it necessary to consult a well-worn Spanish/English dictionary and, during these intervals, Mr. Schwartz asked me about myself. What was I was doing in Granada, where was I staying and how long was I planning to be here? He told me about his home in Ohio, his canning factory, his grand tour of Europe and the chauffeur-driven car that was taking him around Spain. Here, obviously, was a man of some means.

In this way the morning passed pleasantly enough and by lunch time, Mr. Schwartz and I had learnt quite a lot about each other. I had the impression that he was a lonely man, eager for company for, when the time came to say goodbye he seemed reluctant for us to part. Suddenly he said: "Would you join me for lunch? I'm going back to my hotel and I sure would be glad of your company. Y'see I've really enjoyed talking to you."

It was impossible to refuse such an invitation so I said, "You're very kind, Mr. Schwarz and I would love to join you for lunch; but afterwards I must go or my friends will be anxious."

He replied with a big smile. "That's fine. That's just fine."

Outside the gates of the Generalife stood an enormous American car, gleaming white in the sun. Against its bonnet leaned a uniformed chauffeur. He was smoking a cigarette and reading a newspaper but, on catching sight of Mr. Schwartz, hurriedly stuffed it behind his back and stubbed out the cigarette. Leaping to attention, he opened the rear door and we climbed in, sinking deep into the luxurious upholstery. The chauffeur threw me an odd look as we settled down and I felt slightly uncomfortable, but I quickly forgot him and just revelled in the fact that this was turning out to be a thoroughly enjoyable day.

"Which is your hotel?" I asked as we purred along the tree-lined road.

"Oh, it's a cute li'l place here on the Alhambra hill. I guess you'll like it."

The cute little place turned out to be one of the most luxurious hotels in Granada. As we sat on the sunny terrace surrounded by flowers and attentive waiters, admiring the view and enjoying a magnificent lunch of lobster in mayonnaise and champagne, I had to congratulate myself on having decided to do my own thing that morning.

"Where did ya say you're headin' for next?" enquired my rich companion lighting up a cigar as the coffee and liqueurs arrived at the table. I explained that I was with two friends but one of them was returning to Madrid that evening and my girlfriend and I were moving on to Málaga the following morning.

"What d'ya know?" chuckled Mr. Schwartz. "That's just where I'm off to. How you travellin'?"

"By train. We have a kilometric ticket and we can go anywhere we like with it."

"I've heard the trains aren't too good in this part of the world."

"Well, that's true," I admitted, "they're very slow. Our journey from Madrid took seventeen hours."

He threw back his head and roared with laughter revealing a row of gold teeth. "Hey! That sure was some journey. Now, listen here!" He leaned across the table, suddenly serious. "I gotta proposition to make to you – nothin' dodgy you understand. You seen my automobile – it's a big one, holds six, and I get kinda lonesome sittin' there by myself with no one to talk to so why don't you kids come along with me?"

I hesitated, wondering what Anita would think about the idea. "That's a very kind offer," I began, "but…"

"*No* buts," said Mr Schwartz firmly. "You go tell your friend you found yerself a Yank and he's givin' you a lift right down to Málaga tomorrow. Okay?"

I laughed. "That's okay by me and I'll put it to my friend but I can't promise she'll agree. You see, Spanish girls are very old-fashioned and…"

"Yeah, I know – and I like old-fashioned gals. Just tell her there's no funny business about this deal 'cos I'm gonna treat you just like you're my daughters."

The champagne and liqueurs had dispelled any misgivings I might have had and I was determined to persuade Anita to agree. No horrible, dirty train journey tomorrow. We would arrive in Málaga in style. This really was my lucky day.

ଓ ଃଠ

Anita and I arrived back from the station after seeing Desmond off on the train to Madrid only to discover to our horror that he had left with our kilometric tickets still in his pocket. Anita had given them to him to look after, which was not a wise thing to do knowing how absent-minded he tended to be.

We rushed back to the station to consult the stationmaster about our dilemma. He was both helpful and sympathetic, assuring us that all would be well. He would telephone the ticket inspector and the tickets would quickly be recovered from Desmond and sent straight back to Granada on the next train. "Do not worry, *señoritas*, they will be waiting for you in the morning."

"Even if they didn't arrive," I remarked casually to Anita as we walked back to the *pensión,* "at least we would get as far as Málaga because we're not going by train anyway."

She looked at me, her huge eyes wide with surprise. "What do you mean? We can't afford to take a bus when we have perfectly good rail tickets already paid for! No, we can't leave here until we have our tickets."

"I didn't say we were going by bus. I said we wouldn't be taking the train. In fact, we're going by car."

"Are you mad?"

"A fantastic car too, a luxurious six-seater Cadillac with a chauffeur."

"What are you talking about?"

"Oh, and another thing. We're not eating at the *pensión* tonight. We're dining at the Alhambra Palace Hotel. The table's booked for nine o'clock."

Anita stopped walking, took my arm and peered anxiously into my face. "Now please, before you go any further..." she spoke in a gentle, humouring voice of the kind used to address someone who was seriously deranged and prone to bizarre and unpredictable behaviour. "Are you feeling all right?"

"Never felt better," I replied breezily, enjoying her confusion, "especially when I think about that big, expensive meal we're having tonight. It should be even better than the lunch I had today and that was lobsters and champagne."

"You're out of your mind!" snapped Anita, losing her temper. "What are you thinking of being so extravagant? You know we're on a tight budget. We'll quickly run out of money if we're not very careful and there's no way we can eat at the Alhambra Palace Hotel."

"Don't worry!" I giggled. "We're not paying. It will all be taken care of by my good friend Mr. Jerry Schwartz from Ohio."

"Who, for God's sake, is *he?*"

"Just someone I met this morning."

"Do you mean to tell me," she cried, scandalised, "that you have agreed to us having dinner at the most expensive hotel in Granada with a complete stranger?"

"And he's driving us to Málaga tomorrow," I added.

"*Ni hablar!* I won't hear of it."

"But he's not a complete stranger. He's Mr. Jerry Schwartz, a very rich American and I found him in the Generalife. Now don't you think that was clever of me?"

"But we can't do this! Why should he want to wine and dine us and take us to Málaga in his car? What's in it for him?"

"The pleasure of our charming company of course. You shouldn't have such a suspicious mind. He's just a lonely, rich old man in need of company and there's nothing to worry about. He's going to treat us as his daughters."

We arrived back at the *pensión* and, after much persuasion she reluctantly donned her best dress and agreed to come with me for our date. As the Alhambra Palace Hotel was rather far away and we were both wearing stilettos, we decided to take a taxi. Anita became increasingly nervous, protesting that we shouldn't be doing this and that I had no business to be picking up rich Americans in the Generalife. However, when we arrived at our destination, the sight of all that luxury and the prospect of an amazing meal seemed to quell her anxieties and she began to relax. We found our kind host waiting for us in the cocktail bar where he greeted us warmly.

"So this is your Spanish friend!" He smiled approvingly. "Gee, she sure is pretty! I'm a lucky guy. Got myself a blonde and a brunette all in one go!"

"What's he saying? What's he saying?" Anita demanded to know.

"Oh, nothing much: just saying hello," I replied and then, to Mr. Schwartz, "I'm afraid my friend doesn't speak any English."

"Doesn't matter, we're goin' to get along just fine." He grinned at her and she smiled back at him vacantly.

One hour, two bottles of wine and an excellent meal later, Anita had unwound. My role as interpreter, though tedious, was rewarding as I could translate things in a way suitable to the listener.

172

Mr. Schwartz told us about his plans. His itinerary included two nights in Málaga and then on to Algeciras where he would leave the car and take a ferry across to Tangiers. "So you see, gals, you're welcome to come with me all the way to Algeciras. It would be my pleasure."

We were having such a good time that I completely forgot about my date with Juan until suddenly I saw it was eleven fifteen and I remembered I was due to meet him at eleven thirty.

"Look at the time!" I cried. "Anita, we must go home at once. It's past eleven."

"So soon?" asked our host with obvious disappointment. "How about another drink first?"

"Oh no," I replied. "Thank you so much for everything but we must be on our way. Remember, we have a long journey ahead of us so we must go to bed early so that we'll be fresh in the morning. We'll see you tomorrow."

Mr. Schwartz smiled benevolently. "Okay, I guess you're right. I'll get Carlos to run you back."

As we left I heard him murmur under his breath "Good ol' fashioned kids!"

03 &0

"What was the hurry?" asked Anita, puzzled, as she undressed and climbed into bed. "It's quite early you know, and I was enjoying myself."

"Sorry," I said, hastily brushing my hair, "but I have to hurry. I'm late as it is."

"Late for what? What's going on?"

"Sorry again. I forgot to tell you, – what with so much happening. I have to meet Juan at the café down the road."

"Who on earth is Juan? What are you doing? You can't go out now!"

"He's someone I met in the café yesterday and he's promised to take me to the Albaicín. You could come with us if you like."

Anita gave a little gasp of horror. "Desmond was right in what he said about you English girls. He is always right; but I won't let

173

you go. You mustn't go with a strange man to the gypsy quarter in the night. You just don't do that sort of thing in Spain, it's dangerous. No, I won't let you go."

"Don't be such a spoilsport! It will be fun. We're going to a *zambra* with lots of singing and dancing. You know how I like flamenco and I wouldn't miss it for anything. Why don't you come?"

Anita groaned and shook her head in despair. "You must be joking! Nothing would persuade me to go. I value my life. I value my chastity! You must be mad."

"You're so old-fashioned, Anita," I sighed. "But I promise you I can look after myself. Remember, I'm a hardy weed, so stop worrying. Now I must dash or Juan will think I'm not coming."

"I know what it is. It's all that stupid business with Luis. It's affected your brain," she speculated, seeking to justify my outrageous behaviour.

I pulled on my coat and planted a brief kiss on her worried face. "I promise I'll not run away with the raggle-taggle gypsies. See you later."

"I shan't sleep a wink," she threatened. "I'll stay awake until you get back, whenever – or if ever that is."

I slipped out into the night and made my way to the café through streets still thronging with people. When I arrived, at first there was no sign of Juan and I guessed that he must have grown tired of waiting. I was just debating whether to risk death by braving the gypsy quarter on my own, when I spied my self-appointed escort weaving his way towards me between the tables.

"So there you are! I thought you were never coming."

"I'm sorry. I was delayed for all sorts of reasons and Anita didn't want me to meet you. She doesn't trust you or the gypsy quarter."

Juan laughed. "Spanish girls are like that – like my sisters, they aren't allowed out with boys at all. In fact, if a strange boy tried to date any of my sisters I'd soon make him regret it." His eyes gleamed fiercely at the prospect.

"Wow!" I retorted, "You might just as well lock them away like the Moorish kings' harem wives. I can't believe how restricted women are here. But remember, we foreign girls may seem liberated to you but that doesn't mean anyone can take advantage of us."

My companion drew himself up proudly. "What are you suggesting? We Andalusians are men of honour. We have, running through our veins, the blood of the Conquistadors."

"I wouldn't have thought that much of a recommendation!" I laughed. "It's hard to think of a more blood-thirsty band of rogues – wiping out the Indians, stealing all their gold!"

Juan looked hurt. "You English were no better. Your pirates couldn't wait to get their hands on our treasure ships. But never mind about that, let's go and find those gypsies."

Together we climbed the hill towards the Sacromonte, through the dark streets of the Albaicín under a sky glittering with stars. The night was full of mysterious sounds: disembodied voices behind barred windows, a woman's weeping mingled with the crying of a baby, the distant throb of guitars and hissing whispers of love from couples who stood together in the shadow of alleyways. It was a world apart, the world of García Lorca. Begging children darted like fireflies in and out of doorways as we passed, barring our way, wheedling, parting us from our spare pesetas with their tales of starving baby brothers and mothers languishing on their deathbeds. Although the stories were probably fantasies, there could be no doubt about the wretchedness of their condition. Their rags, bare feet and emaciated, small bodies bore witness to the devastating poverty which had driven them out onto the streets. Poverty, that ever-present ghost at the feast, was as much in evidence here in beautiful Granada as elsewhere in Spain.

The Sacromonte where the gypsies lived was pulsating with life. From the doorways of their cave dwellings carved into the side of the hill, floated the sound of nocturnal revels: rhythmic clapping, stamping feet and the rise and fall of husky flamenco voices. The *zambras* were in full swing and for a modest sum we were invited to join them. At the entrance to our chosen cave we were greeted by an enormously fat woman in a multi-frilled, polka-dot dress who proudly informed us that she was related to Carmen Amaya, a famous dancer well-known to London audiences. She ushered us in, her vast breasts and hips heaving and trembling as she moved, as though in protest at the restrictions imposed on them by her tight costume. Here was someone who was definitely not starving.

Inside the dimly-lit cave, the gypsies were seated in a semi-circle clapping to the rhythm of the guitar while two dancers writhed and twisted in the middle of the room. The walls were white-washed and hung with all kinds of decorative objects. There were fans, tapestries, copper pans, pots and plates, knives, guitars, lanterns, wrought-iron trinkets and even a bull's head which glared at us angrily beneath its great curved horns. Everyone seemed to be enjoying themselves and even a couple of tiny children, resplendent in flamenco costume, joined the adult dancers, stamping and clicking their fingers with amazing skill.

Extra rush-seated chairs appeared from nowhere and we took our places in the semi-circle, surrounded by raven-haired beauties, their frilly dresses flowing about them like billowing waves. The dance ended and glasses of sherry were handed round. The performers refreshed themselves, chatting together in their unintelligible *Caló* gypsy language and calling to each other in hoarse voices. In a corner, the guitarist sat bent over his instrument, caressing the strings gently, like a lover, coaxing from them strange ripples of oriental-sounding melody. A bead curtain parted at one end of the room and a frowning young man entered. He was dressed in tight black trousers, a short jacket and frilled pink shirt open to the waist to reveal a tanned, hairy chest. He walked over to the guitarist, placed a hand on his shoulder and stood glaring fiercely at the assembled company, his black, untamed hair falling in strands across his hawkish features. There were shouts of *Olé Paco!* and then the room fell silent, heavy with expectation.

The guitarist struck a few significant chords and Paco threw back his head, closed his eyes and twisted his face into an expression of acute suffering. There followed a long, unearthly wail which rose and fell, varying in intensity, with never a pause for breath. It mounted at last to a passionate, trembling crescendo where it hung agonizingly for a moment before sinking into a moan and fading away to the accompaniment of frenzied *olés*.

"That's a good *canta'or*, " remarked Juan. "And watch this! Here comes a beauty – *olé morena!*"

Across the floor drifted a slender, olive-skinned girl with huge, sultry eyes and pouting lips. Her ink-black hair hung to her waist in a lustrous, thick mane which flew about her face with each proud toss of her head. She stamped and clicked her way towards us, followed by the long rustling train of her scarlet dress, wriggling her body sensuously and provoking howls of anguish from Paco. The dance built up to a fast and furious frenzy, the girl's feet moving like lightning, beating out an intricate rhythm on the floor, arms twisting and weaving in the air, her face contorted in passionate anger, eyes and white teeth flashing.

"Olé! niña de mi alma! Olé guapetona!" yelled Juan. "They're good, aren't they? You won't see dancing as good as this anywhere else in Spain."

Flamenco is infectious and, after a few more drinks, we ceased to be merely spectators and were persuaded to participate in the entertainment. They taught us how to clap in time to the various rhythms and Juan was dragged to his feet by Carmen Amaya's relative who had taken a fancy to him. To everyone's amusement, she hooked her black embroidered shawl round his neck and, still dancing, led him triumphantly to the centre of the room, grinning and winking at us as she did so. She lumbered around him, her thick torso swaying to the music; but old and fat though she was, the graceful movements of her arms and head proved that she had once been a good dancer. Juan of course, would have preferred to have been partnered by the beautiful 'Niña del Peñascal' who continued to captivate him, but it was not to be. Her partner was a wild, dubious-looking character who kept a sullen, watchful eye on her the whole time. I guessed he was the type in whom it would be unwise to inspire jealousy if one valued one's life.

In the course of the night, Paco proved himself not only an excellent *canta'or* but also an imaginative poet. He approached me and hissed in my ear that I had been his sole inspiration for the entire evening and he could not permit us to leave until he had dedicated to us a *copla* which he had just composed. I told him I was both surprised and honoured and he nodded and strode back to his place by the guitarist.

"This *copla*," he announced in a loud voice, "is dedicated to the English *señorita* and her Spanish *novio*."

"*Muy bién!*" yelled the others. "Come on, Paco! Let's hear it!"

The guitarist struck up an improvised introduction and Paco sang us his lines, rendered in the same agonized tones as before. His accent was so strong that I could barely make out the words but Juan told me it was about a fair-haired girl who had travelled from distant shores to join the gypsies of the Albaicín and steal away the hearts of the Granadians. Tears of emotion sprang to my eyes which made me realise I had drunk far too much. The night wore on, as amid laughter and sherry it slowly turned to dawn.

Somehow, and at some time, I managed to get back to the *pensión* although I remembered little about it. I couldn't even recall having said goodbye to Juan but I did notice that Anita seemed to have abandoned her all-night vigil and was curled up in her bed. As I finally crept, exhausted, into mine I could hear her stirring. "At last!" she muttered beneath the blankets, "I've been out of my mind with worry about you. I haven't slept a single wink."

CHAPTER SEVENTEEN

YANKEES

The following morning dawned bright and warm. By the time Anita shook me into wakefulness she had already been down to the station to collect our tickets, had breakfasted, paid our bill and packed her things. She brought me a strong cup of coffee which was more than welcome as a nagging headache was reminding me of my night on the tiles. As I sipped the comforting brew, I regaled her with an account of those escapades and she listened with fascination and incredulity.

"It sounds amazing," she conceded, "but I'd never dare do such a thing."

"Anita," I said, "my mum has always impressed on me that life is short and youth is fleeting so it's as well to make the most of it while it lasts."

"Yes," she nodded doubtfully. "I suppose she's right. Do you know? When I woke up this morning I could hardly believe that I hadn't dreamt all those things that happened yesterday: Mr. Schwartz and the Alhambra Palace Hotel. Are we really going to Málaga with him this morning?"

"Yes!" I exclaimed excitedly, forgetting my headache and leaping out of bed. "We'd better hurry up. He'll be here any minute!"

I was barely dressed when there was a knock at the door and a puzzled maid appeared. "There's a big car outside," she said "and the chauffeur is asking for you."

"That's right," said Anita nonchalantly, "that's our car and we're leaving now." We grabbed our cases and tumbled down the stairs, stifling giggles, to find Carlos waiting for us in the hall. He relieved us of our cases and we followed him out into the sunshine where Mr. Schwartz sat waiting in the car. He was wearing a floppy straw hat and loose, open-neck shirt patterned with palm trees and the words 'Miami Beach – Florida' in huge, gaudy letters. He seemed in excellent spirits and raised his hat to us, grinning cheerfully, the customary cigar protruding from his gold teeth.

"Well, hi gals!" he yelled. "Now hold it! Hold it there a minute! I want you little ladies in my movie." So saying, he produced a small cine camera and poked it through the open window. "Okay, action!" he ordered.

Feeling like film stars, we posed momentarily in the doorway before gliding down the steps as gracefully as we could towards the whirring camera while the *pensión* staff stared at us in amazement. This was a promising start to the day and put us all in the right mood. We jumped in and sat, one either side of our new-found 'Daddy'. He put his arms round our necks, puffed happily at his cigar and said, "Okay, Carlos, take her away! Málaga – here we come!"

As we sped away from Granada, I looked back at the enchanted city and vowed that one day I would return. We climbed high into the mountains, leaving Granada far below, and crossed the wild country that lay between us and the coast, following steep, twisting roads between scrubby bushes, olive groves and high banks studded with cacti and flowering almond trees. The scenery was majestic and beautiful and there was little sign of human life. Once, high above the crags, we saw an eagle circling lazily against the blue. Carlos informed us, cheerfully, that these lonely mountain passes abounded in bandits, thieves, smugglers and other assorted villains. Anita and I were not a little alarmed by this revelation, fearing that the wealthy American could be a prime target should we come across any such stray brigands, but Mr. Schwartz did not share our concern. On the contrary, he found the idea highly amusing. He boasted that his grandfather had tackled fierce Indians in his day and, with such a family background, he wouldn't have any trouble dealing with the odd Spanish bandit should the need arise. Happily it did not, and the journey was both comfortable and uneventful.

We entertained our companion with Spanish and English songs and the time passed quickly. At last we caught our first sight of the Mediterranean away in the distance, a shimmering sheet of turquoise blue glimpsed between umbrella pines. As we drove towards Málaga, the temperature rose and the sun felt increasingly hot. With all the windows down, we were caressed by a stream of warm, pine-scented air, intoxicating as wine, filling our lungs with its heady fragrance.

Málaga was beautiful and exciting with streets of glittering white houses decked with flowers. We drove along a wide boulevard lined on either side with palms. It was thronging with life: people walking, talking, shouting and singing. Dark-eyed little girls dressed like dolls in lacy dresses trotted beside their parents or nursemaids. Lean, brown-limbed boys with bare feet darted among the crowd selling sweets and cigarettes, their faces dirty but smiling, calling out their wares in loud voices. Balloons and flowers were being sold too. On benches under the trees, shabby old men sat around in groups, chatting and spitting. Flocks of girls with red mouths and high stilettos strolled together, arms linked, enjoying the admiration of the youths who stood around watching them. They leaned against trees, smoking and following the girls with their eyes, shouting compliments and mentally undressing them. Then there were old women in black, shuffling along in slippers, fresh-faced young priests, cripples, beggars and blind lottery ticket sellers. Grim civil guards stood sweating in their uniforms and mangy dogs rummaged beneath the benches while numerous carts drawn by skinny mules rattled past.

Mr. Schwartz's destination was the Hotel Miramar, a luxurious establishment of impressive size situated, as its name implied, over-looking the sea. We explained that we had to find ourselves some accommodation and that we would meet him later, but Mr. Schwartz was not in agreement. "What's wrong with this place? Looks okay to me."

"Yes, it's fine for you," I laughed, "but I'm afraid our budget doesn't run to luxury hotels."

"C'mon, Baby," he coaxed, "be my guests!"

I put this suggestion to Anita but she wouldn't hear of it. "We can't stay with him", she protested. "It would put us under an obligation…"

I explained to Mr. Schwartz that my friend insisted that we should be independent although we really appreciated his kindness. "Aw – C'mon! Tell her she'll be sleeping in her own bed, not mine," he laughed.

Despite this reassurance, Anita remained adamant.

"Okay," he shrugged, "you kids are crazy, but if that's the way you want it – I'll see you here around five o'clock and we'll take a trip down town."

And so, to my annoyance, we had to leave our friend to settle himself into his sumptuous hotel while we set off down the side streets in search of some grotty guest house.

CB BD

The evening sun still had strength as Anita and I leaned over the terrace railings, contemplating the scene below. From our viewpoint, high on a pine-clad hill, we could see the town spread out beneath: the promenade, the narrow streets, the bullring, the Miramar Hotel standing among its palm trees, the boats in the harbour and even an American warship that had docked in Málaga.

We were in a hilltop café and Mr. Schwartz was sitting at a nearby table drinking black coffee and chewing thoughtfully at his cigar as he watched with amusement the efforts of two U.S. Marines trying to chat us up in their bad Spanish. The town was full of these Marines swaggering around in impeccable white uniforms and pork pie hats. This particular pair were offering us chewing gum and cigarettes and telling us their names. They seemed enormously tall and blonde with their pale eyes and fresh, well-scrubbed faces, gleaming with health. How different from the short, swarthy and decidedly scruffy Andalusians who stood watching them with undisguised interest!

"Hank," said one of them, pointing to himself, "and Joe. Savee? Ameegos."

Anita giggled and turned her head away. Hank threw back his

head and roared with laughter, displaying two rows of perfect, white teeth, like an advertisement for toothpaste.

"Alright," I said at last, "forget the Spanish. We can get by in English."

"Hey! How about that?" cried Joe. "They speak English!"

By this time we were all in fits of laughter and Mr. Schwartz was calling to us from his table. "C'mon over here you guys an' have a drink!"

We drank vermouth and soda and the boys told us this was their last night in town. Tomorrow they'd be sailing away at crack of dawn.

"Better enjoy yourselves then, I guess," advised Mr. Schwartz. "They say there's a dance tonight at my hotel."

The boys brightened at the prospect. "Wanna come with us?" suggested Joe looking hard at Anita. I interpreted their proposal and could see her weakening visibly before the steadfast gaze of those steely blue eyes. I knew her well enough to be sure she would not be able to resist anything as exciting and exotic as a U.S Marine. She lowered her dark lashes and whispered in my ear: "They are handsome, aren't they?"

"We'll be there," I said.

"Great!" said Hank. "We're gonna have a real good time."

"Hey, now, wait a minute!" interrupted Mr. Schwartz, taking the cigar from his mouth and wafting it across the table as he spoke, "I'm responsible for these gals y'know. I gotta take good care of them." He leaned across the table and fixed the boys with a challenging, mock-stern expression.

"Oh, they won't come to no harm with us, sir," Joe assured him. "They'll be okay with us."

Mr. Schwartz reclined once more into his chair and replaced the cigar between his teeth. He looked from one to the other with slightly screwed-up eyes. "Okay," he drawled, "but mind you guys treat them right. I'm jest warnin' you. You treat these gals right 'cos they're my daughters."

It was touching to see how Mr. Schwarz had taken such a fatherly interest in our welfare. However, having issued this warning, he did not intervene further in the events of the evening and was conspicuous by his absence in the ballroom of the Hotel Miramar.

The dance was in full swing when we arrived for our date with Joe and Hank who were waiting for us in the bar. They ordered more drinks and Joe put his arm round Anita who blushed prettily. Conversation between them proved a little difficult so it wasn't long before they were on the dance floor together where speech wasn't necessary.

Hank led me to a table where we sat and talked. He seemed anxious to talk. Perhaps he needed someone like me, a complete stranger, in whom he could confide knowing we would never meet again. He really didn't like being in the navy, he confessed although perhaps it was better than the army. He missed his family a lot, especially his wife. I was a little surprised to hear he had a wife as he seemed so young.

"Yeah," he said, chewing thoughtfully on his gum. "I gotta wife and she's real pretty." He tugged at something in one of his pockets and produced a brown leather wallet containing a number of photos. He spread them on the table. They were images of the people, places and things which counted in his life. He introduced them to me in turn: Poppa, Momma, Brother Will, friends from High School, the family dog, and, most important of all, his wife. I saw a laughing girl in a summer dress cuddling a round, blonde baby. The pair of them looked back at me as if they could see me now. Oh dear! I mused, what would they think?

Hank pointed to the baby. "That's my son," he said proudly.

"He's lovely," I remarked and there followed a rather awkward silence. Hank's youthful face darkened. "I've not seen him in six months," he sighed, "and I sure miss them, Baby, I sure miss them both. It's real hard." He took my hand as he said this and squeezed it and I suddenly felt very sorry for him. He looked like a little boy in need of comfort and I could see that it was hard for him to suppress the odd tear. They welled up in his grey eyes and he blinked them back again.

"You'll see them again soon," I reassured him, patting his hand.

With an effort he pushed aside his home-sickness and it wasn't too long before he had recovered his spirits. "C'mon! Let's dance!" he said, getting to his feet. "If you call this dancing."

Our companions were disappointed with the band's Latin-American repertoire which they considered 'square' – no jive, no rock, so no chance for the Yankees to show off their talents as 'cool cats'. In view of this, Hank preferred to sit out most of the dances and just talk. He told me about his plans for the future. He had a marvellous career lined up for himself when he left the services. It would bring in loads of money and he would never be unemployed. Such was the nature of his future business that he would always be needed and never, *ever* out of work. I was intrigued. What could it be? After a few futile guesses I gave up.

"Undertaker," he announced, smiling.

"What did you say?" I queried, thinking I had misheard him over the din of the dance band.

"*Undertaker,*" he repeated loudly. "They'll always need me. Honey, one day I'm gonna be rich."

⊂ℨ   �⊃

The evening was drawing to a close. The band was playing a slow, lazy number but only a few couples were still on the floor, shuffling languidly around in an alcoholic daze. The four of us were back together at our table having downed our last drinks. Anita and Joe seemed to have got on reasonably well despite their complete lack of verbal communication.

Hank explained to me that they were going straight back to their ship and had no further use for the odd Spanish pesetas that remained in their pockets, so could we use them? I said jokingly that we could always use money and Hank started emptying his pockets. He placed a pile of pesetas on the table and pushed them in my direction. Joe did the same, piling them in a heap in front of Anita. Unable to understand what we were saying, Anita witnessed these proceedings with increasing horror and confusion. The smile faded from her lips and she tugged urgently at my arm.

"I don't understand. What are they saying? What's going on? Why are they giving us money? I think we should leave at once."

"It's alright," I chuckled, "just keep out of this."

"What do you mean? What are you doing?"

"Oh, shut up and leave this to me!"

"But I'm worried. They mustn't give us money!"

She looked such a picture of outraged consternation that I couldn't resist teasing her for a little longer. "It's alright," I repeated reassuringly, "they're just giving us their money and then they'll walk back with us to our *pensión*."

Anita leapt to her feet. "Do you realize what this means?" she exploded. "You should know what sailors are like! We must get out of here immediately. No! Don't pick up the money! What are you doing?"

I ignored her protests and continued to gather up the notes and coins, tucking them into my purse while the two Americans looked on with satisfied smiles, chewing away at their gum. Anita's face was now white with fear and anger and she seemed on the verge of tears so, in the end, I had to relent and explain the truth.

It was only later that night when she had recovered from the shock, that she could see the funny side of it. Back in the *pensión* she suddenly burst out laughing as we were getting ready for bed.

"That was such an awful moment when they were giving us money! Why didn't you explain what was happening? I really thought…"

"I know what you thought," I said between cleaning my teeth, "it just shows what kind of minds you Spanish have."

I climbed into bed and sank down into the cold sheets. It would soon be dawn and I thought about Joe and Hank back on their ship. They would be gone before the sun rose. I closed my eyes and saw again Hank's fresh, all-American face bending over me as we said goodbye, his grey eyes pleading. "Jest one kiss, Honey, jest one! I aint kissed a gal in a long, long while." As our lips met for the first and last time I hoped the smiling girl in the summer dress wouldn't be too shocked. He's missing you, I wanted to tell her, he loves you and he's really missing you.

CHAPTER EIGHTEEN

SERENADES AND SHERRY

"You'd better keep singing or I'll fall asleep at the wheel!" threatened Carlos as we sped through the dark. The day had been long and we'd left Algeciras late. It was all we could do to keep *ourselves* awake – let alone Carlos, particularly as the seats in the Cadillac were so soft and comfortable. However, fighting off our drowsiness, Anita and I were taking it in turns to sing, chat and otherwise entertain our driver knowing that our lives depended on it. Thankfully, it was now Anita's turn as I had just completed my stint with a reluctant rendering of 'Ten Green Bottles', 'Land of Hope and Glory' and 'Singing in The Rain'. To my irritation, I noticed that Anita was curled up in her corner and appeared to be snoozing. I nudged her mercilessly into wakefulness.

"It's your turn to keep Carlos awake," I reminded her.

She yawned, bleary-eyed, and reluctantly eased herself into a more upright position. In a sleepy voice she started to sing a Castilian folk song about jealous millers and farmers yoking their oxen. I sank back gratefully into my corner and closed my eyes, going over in my mind the events of the day.

I knew that Anita did not feel at all like singing for, apart from her sleepiness, she was engulfed in melancholy at having been parted forever from Mr. Schwartz. Indeed, she had wept copiously as we watched his ferry glide away from the quay at Algeciras and, for the last time, saw his cheerful face under the floppy straw hat. As he receded into the distance, we noticed he was busy with his cine camera recording for posterity our final farewell waves.

Anita remained rooted to the spot as the ferry disappeared into the blue horizon. Even in the short time she had known him and despite the lack of direct communication between them, Anita had grown very fond of Mr. Schwartz. Had she, I wondered, glimpsed in this kindly older man, a fleeting image of the father she had never known?

At last, I persuaded her to leave the quay and we went in search of Carlos whom we had left in one of the harbour bars. With Mr. Schwartz's departure for Tangiers, his duties as chauffeur were ended and it remained only for him to return the Cadillac to Seville where it had been hired. He had offered us a lift to the city provided we were prepared to leave that same night. I, for one, agreed readily for after all, we were becoming quite accustomed to this new, luxurious mode of transport. Anita had some reservations.

The coastal drive from Málaga that morning had been an unforgettable experience. The road was quiet and lined with fragrant umbrella pines framing glimpses of wide, deserted beaches. Here and there, we passed through picturesque fishing villages with white-washed houses, and little boats lined up neatly along the shore. I longed, at times, to leap out of the car and rush down through the pines and fig trees to explore those inviting sands and immerse myself in the blue water. Never had I seen a coast as beautiful as this and the journey seemed all too short. Algeciras was a colourful little port, teaming with cosmopolitan life. Rising defiantly on the other side of the bay was the great, jagged promontory of Gibraltar, an irritating reminder to the Spaniards that we were still in possession of a small chunk of 'their' territory. I found it strange that this barren rock could inspire such primitive tribal emotions.

Anita pointed to it with an accusing finger. "That's ours! Why are you British still there?"

"Because it belongs to us, of course. By right of conquest," I retaliated, suddenly feeling surprisingly patriotic.

Anita turned on me angrily. "What do you mean *right?* You lot have no right to it whatsoever. You can't deny that's Spanish land."

"Nonsense! That's the British Lion you see crouching in the water over there. Haven't you heard of the Treaty of Utrecht?" I teased.

We were still arguing when we reached the bar where Carlos was playing cards with a group of seamen of uncertain nationality. They looked up and flashed their white teeth at us as we approached.

Anita, who was always a little reluctant to enter unfamiliar bars without a reliable male escort, drew back but I pushed her forward, determined that Carlos wasn't going to Seville without us. I knew Anita was far from happy about the arrangement we had made with him. With her usual caution, she had tried to persuade me that we should decline his offer, putting forward the usual arguments: we didn't know him properly, it could put us under an obligation and – horror of horrors – suppose he were to try to rape us by some lonely wayside? It took me some time to convince her that as there were two of us, we were reasonably safe for even if he wanted to, he could hardly rape both of us at the same time! The one who wasn't being raped could bash him over the head with a rock or something. Anyway, he seemed a nice enough man and it seemed unlikely he would suddenly do a 'Jekyll and Hyde'. Eventually she agreed but her misgivings remained.

Carlos ordered us drinks and sided with Anita on the subject of Gibraltar's sovereignty. Others hearing our discussion also rallied to the cause and I realised I was hopelessly outnumbered. In a sudden moment of exasperation, and without checking if there were any civil guards around, I burst out: "It's a good thing for the people who live there that it's not part of Spain. Who wants to live under a Fascist dictatorship?"

There was immediate silence and everyone looked at me and then at each other. I thought: help! What have I said? Why can't I learn to keep my mouth shut? Then a small, quiet man who had been leaning against the bar and listening to our discussion, walked over to our table. "Leave it as it is, that's what I say. I live in La Linea and I go across there every day to work. They live better than us and I earn higher wages than most of the people round here."

So saying, he threw down the stub of his cigarette, screwed it into the floor with his foot and walked out into the sunny street. After that, and to my relief, no one had anything further to say on the subject of Gibraltar.

Carlos had made some friends in the bar and said he wouldn't be leaving for Seville until that night. We arranged to meet him there and were pleased to have a whole afternoon free to explore Algeciras. We walked through the town and along the coastal road, enjoying the sunshine and working up an appetite for lunch.

After about an hour, we came across a little bar-restaurant standing among cacti beside an inviting beach. It was three in the afternoon, we were hot and hungry and this was just what we were looking for. The proprietor was a friendly man who made us very welcome and led us to a table on a small veranda overlooking the beach.

As we tucked into a *paella,* we gazed at the tempting sea and discussed the possibility of taking a dip in the Med. On the off chance, we had that morning optimistically extracted our swimsuits and towels from our cases in the Cadillac boot and stuffed them into a convenient bag. All we needed now was somewhere to change.

The afternoon was warm, as warm as a good summer's day in England. It was hard to believe that this was January and Burgos was probably still blanketed in snow. Anita approached the proprietor and told him of our wish to have a swim. He considered us totally mad to even think about swimming in January, but nonetheless was good-natured enough to humour us and provided not only a room for changing but also, when we emerged from the water, an improvised shower with a watering can.

Now, the memory of that afternoon swim, of the rippling calm water floated through my head and melted into a dream as I drifted into sleep, lulled by the motion of the Cadillac. It was rudely disturbed by the pain of Anita's sharp little nails digging into my forearm as she gripped it and shook me back to life. "Your turn," I heard her saying in an irritable voice. "Wake up and sing to Carlos!"

"How much longer do we have to keep this up?" I complained, reluctant to leave my dream world. "Why can't he listen to the car radio?"

"Good idea!" said Anita, brightening. She tapped him on the

shoulder. "Did you hear that Carlos? Why don't you listen to the radio?"

Carlos grunted and leaning forward, fumbled with some knobs on the dashboard. After a series of crackles and other strange sounds, we were suddenly subjected to a loud, unearthly wailing. "Morocco," he muttered in annoyance and re-tuned the radio. More wailing. Try as he might, we could not pick up any Spanish stations – only North African ones. I realised we had not long left Tarifa, the most southerly point of Spain, so all those radio waves from Morocco were presumably whizzing across the Straits of Gibraltar in strength, jamming out the Spanish radio. Carlos switched it off in disgust and ordered us to resume our singing.

ೞ ಬ

We reached the town of Jerez de la Frontera in the small hours of the morning, our journey having been delayed by a two-hour stop for an evening meal at an inn. It had been rather a romantic meal in an inner courtyard open to the star-strewn sky. The white-washed walls were host to an enormous grapevine which roamed all over them, its gnarled and twisted branches hung with small wrought-iron lanterns. Near the top of one of the walls was an illuminated plaque bearing an image of the Virgin. Yes, it had been a romantic setting for an excellent meal and Carlos had taken care of the bill. At first, Anita had protested about this but I, ever conscious of our steadily dwindling supply of hard-earned pesetas, had kicked her under the table while thanking him for his chivalrous generosity.

Now we were entering Jerez, I had run out of songs and Anita had defiantly fallen asleep. It was hot and stuffy inside the car and smoky too as Carlos had taken to chain-smoking since the departure of Mr. Schwartz. I wound down the window and peered into the darkness, anxious to see what I could of this famous little town, home to Spanish sherry. Unfortunately, I could see very little, just a few dark streets and a signpost indicating the direction of Seville. However, to my surprise Carlos did not take that road but instead turned the Cadillac down a narrow side street. Remembering Anita's apprehensions, I felt slightly worried.

"Carlos," I said leaning across to him, "where are we going?"

"I'm thirsty," he mumbled biting on his cigarette. "It's hot and I'm thirsty. How about you?"

I had to admit that I was too. After all that singing my throat was as dry as dust.

"Well, we've come to the right place," chuckled Carlos, "and I happen to know a very good *bodega*. Don't you want to tell your friends in England that you've drunk sherry in the place where it's made?"

"Well yes, I suppose so; but isn't it a bit late? Will it still be open?"

Carlos roared with laughter. "They never stop drinking here," he assured me. "Drink all night long."

He drew the car up alongside a dirty little doorway, which could even rival the entrance to Don Federico's academy. Just inside, I could make out a dimly lit flight of stairs running down, I guessed, to some deep cellar from which drifted the sound of drunken laughter and the twang of a guitar.

Carlos switched off the engine, rolled up his shirt sleeves and turned to me with a smile. "Here we are," he said, "best place in town for sherry."

For a moment I hesitated. It didn't look the sort of place where you would find women other than those of dubious character.

"Er... you go. I'll stay here with Anita. Sherry's not very thirst-quenching."

"A glass of wine then?" urged Carlos. "Come on down! I'll look after you. There's a fabulous flamenco singer down there. They say he's the best in the whole of Andalusia."

This was tempting as I could never resist flamenco and I could just hear, coming from below, something that sounded very promising. Overcoming my reluctance I decided this was something too good to miss.

"Alright, but I'm not leaving Anita."

"No! no! She must come too," insisted Carlos.

In fact Anita was beginning to stir, roused by our conversation and the sudden extinguishing of the car's engine. She raised her head and looked around sleepily. "Where are we?" she yawned. "Seville already?"

"Jerez," I told her with excitement, "where the sherry comes from and we've stopped for a drink."

"Where?" she enquired suspiciously.

"In there," I replied waving a hand in the direction of the doorway. "I know it looks a bit seedy but there's a fantastic flamenco singer – the best in Andalusia. Can't you hear him?"

Anita took one look at the shabby doorway and shook her head firmly. "No way! I don't like flamenco and, even if I did, you wouldn't get me in there. No woman who values her reputation would be seen dead in a place like that!"

Carlos laughed. "Oh, it's not that bad, and I'm here to take care of you. Let's go! It sounds like they're having a good time down there."

From the depths of the *bodega* rose a chorus of animated shouts and guffaws.

Anita seized my arm. "Listen to them! They sound like a pack of wild animals. Let Carlos go on his own! I'm not going down there and neither are you if you have any sense. If you do, the chances are you won't come back in one piece!"

Carlos was growing impatient with our arguing. He opened the car door and climbed out, stretching himself and taking in deep breaths of the night air.

"Well, while you two decide what you want to do, I'm going to have my drink. I'm parched. See you in a minute." With this he locked the car and disappeared down the stairs.

I felt like a pet dog left on the back seat, awaiting the return of its owner and I was annoyed with Anita for being such a killjoy. Thanks to her, I had not only forfeited the drink I so much needed, but also the chance of hearing the best flamenco singer in Andalusia.

"I despair of you," sighed Anita as we sat waiting for Carlos. "You just don't seem to understand about Spain. We're not in Castile now, remember! This is Andalusia and they're very old-fashioned here in their attitude to women. The people have all this Moorish and Gypsy blood and the men are like wild beasts when they're drunk."

"I think you're exaggerating," I said sulkily. "And anyway, you can't tell me anything about dangerous Spanish males; not after living with Vázquez!"

At that moment, Carlos reappeared bearing two glasses of wine which he handed to us through the rear window. "They'll be up in a moment," he said, "that's just to keep you going till they come up. They're bringing the sherry and the flamenco singer."

"Who are?" cried Anita, sitting bolt upright in alarm. "What are you saying?"

"That lot down there, of course." Carlos grinned and lit a cigarette, leaning against the side of the car. "I've told them there are two beautiful *señoritas* up here in need of refreshment and entertainment."

"How could you say such a thing?" Anita's face was reddening. "How embarrassing! Go down at once and tell them not to come!"

"Too late!" he chuckled. "They're on their way up now. Here they come!"

The sound of rowdy merry-making grew ever louder and we saw the dark shapes of what seemed like dozens of men emerging from the doorway. Anita shrank back in terror as they approached. They lurched towards us shouting drunkenly in their heavy Andalusian accents, waving bottles and glasses above their heads, and filling the still air with their raucous laughter. Anita clung to me and I could feel her trembling. "This is awful!" she whimpered, "I knew we shouldn't have come with Carlos."

They clustered round the car, bending to leer at us through the windows, thrusting forward their bottles and inviting us to refill our glasses.

"*Que guapas!*" shouted one of them peering at us with semi-focused eyes and then, turning to Carlos: "Two in one go you lucky bastard! Tell us how you do it!"

"Yes, what's he got that we haven't?" yelled another.

Anita buried her face in her hands. "I think I shall die of shame!" she said dramatically.

Carlos pushed them away from the car. "Wind down the window!" he ordered. "They're bringing up the flamenco singer now."

Somebody shouted, "Make way for Pepe!" "Where's Mario?" called another voice. "Ah, there he is! Over here, Mario!"

Out of the gloom stepped a plump, middle-aged man with a guitar. He smiled at us with half-closed eyes, a cigarette smouldering at the corner of his mouth, his black Andalusian hat set at a jaunty angle. He struck a few chords on his guitar then came over and took up his position near the bonnet of the Cadillac. Up the stairs came yet another group of men who appeared to be half carrying, half dragging something between them. Brushing aside Anita's protests, I wound down the window to get a better view of what was going on. I then realised that what they were hauling through the doorway was a man who appeared to be semi-conscious.

"Wake up, Pepe!" shouted one of his companions. "Here are two *señoritas* come all the way from Algeciras to hear you sing."

Someone slapped him on the cheeks and he rallied a little, opening a pair of dazed eyes and peering around. He was lean and dark with an unshaven face and thick, black sideburns reaching almost to his jaw. He was dressed in a torn, wine-stained shirt, faded trousers and rope-soled sandals. Round his waist he wore a wide *faja*, a sort of sash reminiscent of characters in a Goya painting. Mario struck a few more encouraging notes on his guitar and someone called out: "Give him another drink!"

I leaned out of the window. "Is this the flamenco singer?" I enquired of the men. They nodded vigorously. "That's him. Best in the whole of Spain."

"But he's dead drunk! He can't even stand upright, never mind sing."

The men laughed. "The more he drinks the better he sings," said one of them. "You'll see. *Oye!* Over here Pepe! The *señoritas* are waiting."

"He's famous, you know," somebody said, "everyone's heard of Pepe."

"Pepe, Él del Cuchillero," added the first man, "Son of the Knife Grinder. You're lucky to have found him."

Meanwhile, Pepe, still supported by his friends, was being plied with yet more alcohol. Someone thrust a glass into his hand

and someone else filled it from an earthenware carafe. He swigged it down in one gulp and the glass was immediately replenished. I expected to see him collapse again but, surprisingly, it seemed to have the opposite effect. Considerably revived, he broke away from his entourage and staggered forward to inspect us. He stood beside the car, swaying slightly, scrutinising us with jet-black eyes.

"Now we know what it feels like to be an animal behind bars in a zoo!" I whispered to Anita.

"Well, it's your fault," she retorted, "it's all your fault, being so crazy about flamenco: just like a foreign tourist."

I knew this last remark was intended as a strong insult and it brought home to me just how annoyed she was.

"Well, what do you think of them?" asked Carlos of the assembled company. He was grinning with satisfaction, showing us off as a farmer would a pair of prize pigs.

Pepe, Son of the Knife Grinder gave a slow smile and clamped his hand to his heart.

"I am blinded by their beauty," he lisped. "They are as beautiful as dawn itself. This one," here he pointed to Anita, "has eyes that sparkle more brightly than the stars; and this one," indicating me, "has hair golden as the rising sun." The onlookers, who had fallen silent, all nodded and muttered their agreement.

"Aha!" I said, giving Anita a nudge, "you have to admit these Andalusians certainly know how to pay compliments."

I knew the one thing she could never resist was flattery and already I saw that she was weakening.

"Well, yes," she admitted, "as compliments go, I suppose they're not too bad. Not a patch on Desmond's, of course."

"My song," said Pepe, "is dedicated to their loveliness."

He lurched over to where Mario was standing, his guitar at the ready, and the crowd surged forward, shouting encouragement.

Someone had thoughtfully brought up a chair for the benefit of the guitarist who sat down to tune his instrument. Meanwhile, Pepe drained his glass and tossed it into the air where it was deftly caught by one of the bystanders. Mario bent over his guitar and struck a series of rousing introductory notes. The moment we had all been waiting for had arrived.

Pepe's eerie flamenco voice cut the stillness of the night with strange, trembling song, rising and falling, passionate and spine-chilling while the guitar followed him, accompanying each wild, improvised sequence with appropriate chords. The others muttered *olé!* and other comments of approval at the end of each *cante*. From time to time, between songs, he would refresh himself with yet more wine and, oddly, it really did seem that his singing improved with every glass.

Anita and I were handed sherry through the car window as our serenade continued. Having exhausted the theme of our loveliness, he went on to sing about gypsy lovers, dark-eyed girls, impending death and unrequited love. Many of the words and phrases must have had bawdy double meanings. As a foreigner, they were lost on me but were obviously significant to the men who responded with ribald laughter while Anita blushed, clapping her hand to her mouth.

Sometimes, during more lively passages, the others would join in with rhythmic hand-clapping and the scene gradually acquired the atmosphere of a street party. The whole situation was so extraordinary and unreal that it was hard to believe I was not dreaming.

At last, and with some reluctance, Carlos decided it was time for us to make a move. Pepe had sung his last song, the alcohol having at last taken its toll. He collapsed once more into the arms of his friends who, by this time, were not in a much better state themselves.

With their drunken farewells still ringing in our ears, we backed slowly out of the narrow street and onto the Seville highway.

I said: "That was a good idea of yours, Carlos, stopping at that place. But we weren't expecting a party in our honour!" I turned to Anita. "What did you think of Pepe, Él del Cuchillero?"

"I don't like flamenco," was her sleepy reply. "How many more times do I have to tell you?" But she didn't sound very convincing.

CHAPTER NINETEEN

BLOOD ON THE DANCE FLOOR

We quickly discovered two things about Seville: that the streets were narrow and the men were jealous.

The fact that the streets in the old quarter, known as the Barrio de Santa Cruz, were extremely narrow was brought home to us forcefully when we first arrived there at dawn on our first day. Carlos, who was himself a Sevillano, had recommended a cheap *pensión* which he knew of in that area and had insisted in driving us to the very door. We nosed our way through a maze of tortuous little lanes which all the time seemed to be getting narrower until, at last, the crunch came. Literally! The Cadillac, our beautiful, impressive Cadillac, designed to sail through the wide and spacious avenues of North American cities, had jammed fast between the walls of a street which could just about accommodate a man leading a mule.

Carlos swore lustily and put it into reverse gear. The wheels spun impotently but the bonnet was firmly wedged and refused to budge. Carlos swore even louder and Anita, who was not used to such language, put her hands to her ears.

We got out, climbed over the bonnet and started pushing with Carlos still at the wheel and the engine screaming its disapproval. But, strain as we might, it was all to no avail.

Carlos, careless of the fact that he was waking half the neighbourhood, shouted for help and, after a few moments, a little man appeared from nowhere and came running to our assistance. He wore a heavy coat and carried an enormous bunch of keys from which I deduced he was the local *sereno* or night watchman whose job it was to tour the streets throughout the hours of darkness, unlocking doors for nocturnal residents. I had come across these *serenos* in Madrid and was always astonished by their constant availability. You could be in a completely deserted street, locked out at any hour of the night, and all you had to do was clap your hands a few times for a *sereno* to appear out of thin air like a genie from Aladdin's lamp.

This one came trotting up to us, keys jangling, smiling and helpful as only a *sereno* could be at such an hour. All three of us now pushed and heaved to dislodge the Cadillac but our combined strength plus the reverse gear were still insufficient. The *sereno* said not to worry; he would go and find some friends who would certainly be able to get us out of our fix.

He returned shortly with three burly chaps in blue workman's dungarees. Their muscular arms, bulging beneath their rolled-up shirtsleeves, looked strong enough to shift a tank.

Predictably, the added brute force of the *sereno's* stalwart friends did the trick and, with the sickening sound of scraping metal, the car was finally freed from its imprisonment. Carlos surveyed the damaged wings with deepening gloom. "How am I going to explain *this* to the boss?" he muttered.

"That you were in a traffic jam?" suggested Anita, "And a lorry tried to squeeze by and rammed you into a wall? No, that won't do. They'd want to know the number of the lorry."

"Don't worry," he said philosophically, "I'll think of something. Now you girls had better find your *pensión*. It's down this street, to the right."

Regretfully we took our leave of Carlos, for he had been a good friend, but that same day he had to drive for another client and we knew we wouldn't see him again. The Cadillac backed away round the corner and was soon gone as were the *sereno* and his friends, who had disappeared as swiftly as they had come.

Anita and I were left standing alone with our cases on the cobblestones of the Barrio de Santa Cruz as the first streaks of dawn crossed the dark sky. We walked along the quiet street with its picturesque lanterns and flower-decked balconies. In the half-light we could just make out pretty, tiled patios behind traceries of wrought iron reminding us of Granada.

At the end we turned right, as instructed, and found ourselves in an even narrower street: so narrow, in fact, that by stretching out our arms we could touch both the opposite walls. The street curved away round a corner and as we approached the bend we heard, breaking the early morning silence, a bleating sound and the rattle of buckets.

A woman was sitting milking a black goat by one of the entrances and behind her was a young boy holding the tethers of two more. The woman was humming softly under her breath in time to the rhythmic splash of milk in the bucket. Standing just inside the entrance, watching her, was a girl holding a large pitcher.

The woman looked up at us and smiled and Anita asked her where we could find the *pensión*. In reply she jerked her head towards the entrance and the girl nodded in confirmation. It seemed we had come to the right place at the right time, our arrival having coincided with the milk for our breakfast coffee.

CS   SO

I had harboured the faint hope that, with all the many diversions of the last few days: Mr. Schwartz, the U.S. Marines, our party at Jerez and now our arrival in this most exciting of Spanish cities, perhaps Anita might have forgotten about Desmond Brocklebank. In fact, for a time, this really did seem to be the case for she had hardly mentioned him recently; but now, as we sat under some tall palm trees in the María Luisa Park, I noticed, to my dismay, the return of all those familiar and ominous signs. There were the sighs, the dreamy far away look and the reflective, flickering smile – all worrying portents of the revival of her crazy infatuation. Something had to be done about it.

"What are you thinking about?" I ventured to ask her, suspecting that her answer would confirm my worst fears. She gave another deep, contented sigh and leaning back on the bench, gazed starry-eyed, up into the trees.

"I am thinking," she mused, "about all those interesting things Desmond told me in Granada: about the progress of the Human

Soul, Buddhism and the Noble Eight-fold Path and... the philosophy of Hegel, his ideas of Mind and Nature being one. I didn't know about any of these things but... when *he* explains them they become so clear."

"Hmm, yes," I said doubtfully, "but you were thinking about something else too, weren't you? What are all those smiles in aid of?"

She laughed happily. "Ah, I was thinking what a wonderful, romantic man Desmond is and about all the lovely things he called me: like Aphrodite, Goddess of Love! No one has ever called me that before. And do you know? I think he is a little in love with me. Isn't that marvellous? Yes, I really think he is in love with me!"

"But you can't be serious about him," I protested, "he's well over forty and mad as a hatter."

She stared at me in astonishment. "How can you say that? Of course I'm serious. You don't understand. Oh, how I long to be back in Madrid so that I can see him again!" Things were even worse than I had feared.

"Anyway," she continued, "you're a fine one to preach! How about your crazy boyfriends? That Julio is a madman if ever I saw one and as for Luis – well, you know what I think of *him*."

"Julio is *not* my boyfriend," I retorted, smarting from her counter attack, "not really. He just thinks he is. And you can leave Luis out of this because you know very well I'm through with him."

"Alright, alright!" she said soothingly. "No need to be so irritable. Let's not quarrel. Let's talk about something else."

"Like the Sevillanos?" I suggested. "Don't you think they're a good-looking lot?"

"Are they? I hadn't noticed."

Now Anita was such an exceptionally attractive girl that she was never short of male attention. This was certainly true in Seville where the young men seemed particularly susceptible to feminine beauty. Wherever we went, those roving, Andalusian eyes followed her, and numerous imaginative compliments tumbled from their lips as she passed by. But Anita, despite being a connoisseur of *piropos* (compliments), still had her head in the clouds. It was full of thoughts about Desmond and I believed her when she said she hadn't even noticed them. I decided that, in the circumstances, it might be a good idea to distract her by drawing her attention to the local talent.

"Look!" I muttered. "Look at those two over there! They're really good-looking and they've been watching us for ages, and now they're coming over this way!"

Anita stood up abruptly and brushed down her skirt. "Let's go!" she said. "We've still got lots to see here."

"But have you seen the Giralda Tower?" asked one of the boys who had overheard her. "It's the pride of Seville, the most beautiful thing in the whole of Spain – yet it is as nothing compared with your beauty!" His eyes swept over her as he spoke.

Anita smiled with delight but pretended not to hear. "Come on!" She linked arms with me urging me to quicken my pace.

"Let us show you Seville," suggested her admirers hurrying alongside us. "Let us be your guides! But first, we could have a drink together."

"No thanks," said Anita but she was still smiling which I took as a hopeful sign.

"Coffee perhaps?" they persisted. "We know a good café just round the corner; and then we'll show you the Giralda and the Torre de Oro and Triana – that's the gypsy quarter – if you like."

Seeing that Anita was weakening I said I thought that sounded a good idea and I was dying for a cup of coffee.

Delighted, they introduced themselves as Ricardo and Luciano, medical students. It was amazing to me how many medical students there seemed to be around. The whole country was swarming with them and I guessed there would never be a shortage of doctors.

Ricardo, who was tall, dark and handsome, attached himself to Anita and, since she had a passionate interest in all things medical, they were soon deep in conversation. This looked hopeful and I was optimistic that my plan might work.

So engrossed was I in observing the progress of my project that I almost forgot about Luciano who was now saddled with my company, a definite second best I imagined, since his friend had grabbed Anita.

"I wonder what it is about Ricardo," I heard him say wistfully. "What makes him so popular with all the girls?"

I realised I had been watching the other couple intently and Luciano had interpreted this as jealousy on my part. I looked at him for the first time. He was shorter than me but not unattractive with soft, brown eyes and a pleasant smile.

"You mean your friend over there?" I feigned surprise. "I don't think there's anything special about him. Don't imagine I was thinking about *him*. It's just I had my mind on something else."

"Well, that's a relief!" laughed Luciano. "How about another coffee?"

We spent the rest of the day with our new friends and we couldn't have found better guides. We were taken to the Giralda Tower, a beautiful Moorish minaret crowned with a piece of Gothic nonsense, presumably to make it look less heretical when it became a Christian church. Beside it was a broad square, the Plaza de Naranjos, appropriately named after the orange trees that adorned it. We wandered along the banks of the River Guadalquivir and were shown another landmark, the Torre de Oro. Nearby was a bridge which opened to allow the passage of vessels, not unlike our own Tower Bridge but smaller, and across the river was mysterious Triana, famous for its gypsies. They offered to take us there but Anita said she would rather not explore it at the moment.

They wined and dined us and eventually, as the afternoon turned to evening, invited us to a dance later that night. We were thoroughly enjoying ourselves, Anita was in good spirits and, when we returned to the *pensión* to change, there was no mention of Desmond. Everything was going exactly according to plan.

ɔʒ ଚଠ

Despite the fact that the hall where the dance was being held was large, there was little room to move around as it was packed solid with people. After a bit, Luciano and I gave up any attempt at dancing properly and just stayed on the spot, swaying to the music.

It was very hot and stuffy, the air thick with cigarette smoke and reeking of human sweat mixed with assorted perfumes. There were beads of perspiration on Luciano's forehead, trickling down from his damp, brown curls. His hand, clasping the small of my back, felt hot and sticky.

The band was playing a lively *pasodoble* and the great sea of couples heaved and throbbed all around us, shoving us this way and that, treading on our feet and sometimes nearly knocking us over.

Unperturbed by these discomforts, Luciano was trying to tell me about his studies. He was, he explained, intending to become a pathologist one day. "We're starting a very interesting part of the course, actually dissecting human bodies. It's quite fascinating!"

"Oh no, I don't believe it! The last person I went dancing with was a future undertaker. Is there no getting away from you ghouls?"

Luciano laughed. "You mustn't think of it that way. After all, the body is only a machine like any other, with bits and pieces that keep it going. So when it goes wrong or stops working altogether, it's intriguing to find out why; to look for the cause of the trouble – just like you would a car engine."

"Yes, I suppose so," I said, unconvinced.

"You'd be amazed if you could see what there is inside you and what's going on in there right now. Your heart pumping away, your lungs expanding and contracting, your brain buzzing with signals and impulses, your digestive system breaking down that meal we had earlier, your kidneys busy purifying your blood – it's incredible! And the strangest thing is that we take it all for granted. We think a person is what we see on the outside but what about the hidden bits we can't see?"

"I think I would prefer not to see those bits," I confessed.

"Aha! You women are all alike. Squeamish."

"Not all of us. Anita's a nurse and she's not at all squeamish. She's a bit like you. By the way, where is she? I haven't seen her for ages."

"Enjoying herself, I think," he replied. "The last time I saw her she was being chatted up by at least half a dozen boys. You see, there are loads of our friends here and, well, she's a very pretty girl."

"Yes," I said, feeling triumphant, "she is, and I'm so glad she's having fun."

"She'd better be careful though, Ricardo can be very jealous."

"Why don't we go and find them?" I suggested, feeling slightly anxious.

We pushed our way, through the mass of pulsating humanity, to the side of the dance floor where we had last seen the couple. They were still there but no longer alone. A group of admiring men had gathered around Anita who was engaged in flirtatious conversation with a black-eyed individual in a red shirt. Ricardo was not looking at all pleased. The small moustache above his lips twitched in disapproval as he stood glaring at them. This, Luciano whispered in my ear, was a bad sign. "Could be fireworks if this goes on!" he commented with relish.

In an effort to remove Anita from the unwelcome company of his friends, Ricardo kept suggesting to her that they should dance again. She, on the other hand, was enjoying all the attention and found various excuses not to do so. "But I'm tired, Ricardo, and my shoes are pinching. Later. We'll dance later."

The young man in the red shirt handed her a drink. "Perhaps this will refresh you, niña," he grinned, "and give us a few more minutes to enjoy your beauty before he snatches you away again."

Anita glanced at her admirer coquettishly and switched on her dazzling smile, raising her glass seductively to her lips. Encouraged, he took a step closer. His eyes, narrowed to slits, smouldering with desire. Ricardo grabbed Anita by the wrist and jerked her away from him.

"Just watch it, Miguel!" he hissed between clenched teeth.

"He's furious!" Luciano whispered in my ear. "He can't stand competition. It's a matter of pride."

"Don't you think we ought to create some sort of diversion? You talk to Ricardo and I'll have a word with Anita."

Luciano nodded and approached his friend, clamping an

amiable hand on his shoulder. "So there you are, Ricardo. How about a drink?"

I went over to Anita and drew her to one side. Strangely, our usual roles were now reversed and I had become the restraining influence. "Look," I said, "can't you see Ricardo's getting really jealous?"

She laughed. "Yes. Isn't he silly?"

"But remember what you told me about Andalusian men? All that about them becoming like wild animals after a few drinks?"

"That was different. Those men in Jerez were all strangers: just a band of drunken rough-necks. We know Luciano and Ricardo and these are all their friends."

"You shouldn't flirt with that fellow in the red shirt. Ricardo doesn't like it."

"Who cares? He's not my *novio*. Anyway, the one in the red shirt is very nice. He said my lips are like carnations."

At that moment, the subject of our conversation came over to join us, taking advantage of Ricardo's temporary absence. He seemed not in the least deterred by the warning. His piercing eyes examined me momentarily. *"Buenas noches, señorita,"* he murmered briefly before turning his attention once more to Anita. He seized her hand, pressed it passionately to his lips and then drew her towards him. "Dance with me!" I heard him mutter in a low breathless voice. "All evening I have been longing for this moment. Since I first set eyes on you I have been tormented by your beauty."

My heart sank as I saw her readily agree. He clasped her to him in a fierce embrace and drew her into the swaying masses on the dance floor. I hoped fervently that Ricardo would not notice what had happened and that Luciano would keep him occupied for a little longer. But it was not to be. His sharp ever-watchful eyes immediately spotted them and for a moment he froze, his face registering blind rage as the colour drained from his cheeks.

Shoving Luciano aside, he charged onto the dance floor like an enraged fighting bull, pushing his way roughly through the dancing bodies until he reached Anita and her partner. Seizing his rival by his red shirt, he tore him away from her and dealt him a thunderous blow to the face which sent him flying between the startled couples to land heavily on the floor, some feet away. Anita screamed and rushed to my side where she clung to me in consternation. The dancing couples, interrupted by the disturbance, drew back to allow space for this unexpected cabaret. Luciano and his friends lit cigarettes and settled down to watch.

Ricardo was standing over his fallen enemy, fists clenched. "You drunken son-of-a-bitch!" he snarled. "You keep your filthy hands off that girl! *I'm* the one who brought her to this dance and *I'm* the one she dances with. Is that understood?"

Miguel of the red shirt rose slowly to his feet, spitting blood and the odd tooth, his eyes blazing with fury. "I'm going to kill you for this!" he hissed.

Ricardo threw off his jacket and pulled his tie from his neck. Miguel passed a hand over his gory mouth and then flew at his rival, landing a body blow that had him temporarily winded at which the crowd roared their approval. They seemed to be watching this entertainment in much the same way as they would a bullfight. The two were now raining an avalanche of blows at each other with a ferocity that was terrible to behold. Here indeed was the Green-eyed Monster at his most triumphant!

Anita clutched my arm tightly, watching the spectacle with a horror very slightly tinged with pride. "Look!" she cried. "What did I tell you about Andalusians? They're fighting like wild beasts – and all because of me! We must stop them."

"Yes, stop them somebody!" I cried out. "Can't any of you do something? They're hurting each other. Luciano – *do something!*"

Luciano looked surprised at my concern. "I'm not going to interfere," he said. "It's their business. They've got to settle it one way or the other. It's a matter of honour."

"How stupid! You're all crazy!"

"You don't understand," said one of the onlookers. "You're foreign so you don't understand. We Andalusians are a very proud people and honour is important to us."

"You're just a blood-thirsty lot of hooligans and you're enjoying every minute of this."

Everyone laughed and Anita, who was now in tears, said:

"They're right. There's nothing we can do about it."

Desperately, we shouted to Ricardo to stop but our words fell on deaf ears. They continued to pound away at each other relentlessly to the ever-increasing excitement of the spectators. Most of the couples had now stopped dancing and were pushing forward to get a better view. Even the band was taking a lively interest. They stopped playing and sat down to watch from their advantageous position on the raised dais.

The crowd began to take sides and I heard several men making bets on the winner. The air rang with shouts. "Come on, Miguel, let him have it!" "Go on! Kill him, Ricardo!" The males, all brimming with testosterone, were certainly enjoying themselves but some of the girls were frightened and covered their eyes, crying *"Ay! Ay! Ay!"* Others giggled.

I looked around to see if someone in authority, perhaps the manager of the dance hall or the caretaker might appear and put a stop to the fight but there was no sign of any such person although one of the girls said someone had gone to fetch the police.

Although Miguel was a fierce fighter, Ricardo seemed to have the advantage due to his superior height and having landed the first damaging blow. Moreover, Miguel's face was now pouring with blood which hampered his vision. The end was near. Catching his opponent in an unguarded moment, Ricardo struck him a shattering left hook to the jaw which sent him reeling back to collapse, senseless, on the floor. I felt slightly sick and not a little worried about Miguel who was lying very still.

"Go and see to him, Luciano," I urged, "Ricardo may have killed him."

Luciano laughed. "That's nothing! Nothing a bucket of cold water won't cure. Now if it had been knives – as it could well have been – then that would be a different matter."

I turned to Anita. "Let's get out of here!" I whispered.

Ricardo, whose face was bruised and puffy but otherwise seemed alright, was putting on his jacket and tie. Honour had been satisfied and he seemed well pleased with himself.

Not so pleased were those men who had placed bets on Miguel. An argument had broken out about Ricardo's tactics and others joined in. There were heated exchanges and, to my horror, these quickly developed into violent scuffles. Soon the whole place was in uproar.

Meanwhile, Miguel had recovered his senses and was helped to his feet. He stood swaying unsteadily and looking about him in a daze, shaking his head and wiping his battered face with his sleeve. The floor was spattered with blood and everywhere people were fighting. The dance had turned into an ugly brawl and all because of Anita.

I grabbed her arm and pushed her towards the exit. "That's it!" I said. "Let's get out quick!"

"Yes," she agreed, trembling, "it's terrible. We've got to get out of here."

Luciano noticed our retreat and rushed over. "Where are you going?" he wanted to know. "Wait for us!"

"Just going to the cloakroom. Back in a moment," I lied.

No sooner had we reached the exit, than a band of stern-faced civil guards arrived and pushed their way in through the door, roughly thrusting people aside and brandishing weapons. We got out in the nick of time to avoid further trouble and ran, fleet-footed, through the streets until we were safely out of reach.

"*Que horror!*" panted Anita. "What a disgusting scene! I've had quite enough of these hot-blooded Andalusians. Let's go back to Madrid tomorrow! Back to civilization: back to *Desmond!*"

CHAPTER TWENTY

MOUNTAIN GOATS

One of my favourite haunts in Spain's Capital City was the Retiro Park. On a previous visit I had taken digs in the Calle Ibiza which was within easy walking distance of the park. I used to wander daily along its paths, discovering little secret paved areas where one could bask in the sun, sheltered from any wind by cypress hedges, and watch the old ladies sitting on benches, gossiping and nursing their pet dogs. I also delighted in seeking out the various statues that nestled among the rose bushes and I enjoyed strolling beside the Estanque. This was a large lake bobbing with little rowing boats where the *madrileños* liked to relax on warm evenings. Sometimes, Rafael and I would hire one of these boats and spend a pleasant half hour rowing to the accompaniment of Spanish music played over a loud speaker. Each boat had a number and when our time was up, the number would be called and we would have to head for shore.

But on this particular day there were neither boats nor music on the lake. It was mid winter, the trees were bare, there were no roses and the park was practically empty. Nevertheless, even in this inhospitable season, the Retiro still seemed beautiful. I was aware that someone was walking beside me and I felt a warm glow of happiness. I looked up and saw the handsome, pensive face of the man I loved, introspective and silent as usual, locked in a private, impenetrable world that was his alone. The wind was bitterly cold but his tall form, close to my side, shielded me from its knife-edge. *Luis!* I said and reached out to touch him but my hand felt nothing but the cold January air and my voice, uttering his name, was heard only by a solitary cat stalking along the path ahead. What was happening to me? Was I going mad? So strong had become my passionate longing for him that it was even causing me to hallucinate! Despite all efforts to banish him from my thoughts, his ghost haunted me constantly, tormenting me every night by entering my dreams and now it even appeared in daydreams: dreams of what might have been here in Madrid. I cursed my imagination.

I stood beside the lake looking down into the water at my own reflection, perhaps to assure myself that I really was alone. A sad, plain girl stared back at me, her face pinched with cold, straggly hair whipped into thin strands. Could this pathetic, unattractive creature be me?

Overcome by unhappiness, I collapsed onto a nearby bench and, knowing I was quite alone, allowed myself a thoroughly good howl. After a while the black mood passed and I felt a sense of relief. I dried my swollen eyes, blew my nose, and tried to collect my thoughts. All this *had* to stop, I told myself severely. Things couldn't go on like this. I had to forget him: forget him completely.

I shivered as a biting gust of wind swept about me. The grey clouds parted for a minute and a few pale streaks of weak sunshine cast mottled shadows across the path. In the distance, I saw two figures walking towards me; they were Desmond and Anita from whom I had earlier made my escape. As they came close I saw that he had his arm round her and they were looking very happy. Anita spotted me and waved. "Where have you been?" she called. I wiped my face hurriedly, hoping they would not notice that I had been crying.

What an odd pair they made! She was looking as lovely and well groomed as ever. No amount of buffeting by the wind could disarrange those short, thick curls and her face was not pinched. On the contrary, it was aglow with warmth and happiness and her eyes were, as usual, sparkling. Beside her, the tall figure of Desmond, lean and Quixotic, looked strangely out of place. He was still wearing his ageing duffle coat with the missing toggle, and the rest wrongly fastened so that one side of his coat was shorter than the other.

"What on earth are you doing here, sitting all by yourself?" Anita demanded to know. "Aren't you cold? After all that lovely warm weather down in the south, it feels really cold."

"No doubt you are familiar," said Desmond, "with that proverbial Spanish saying: *The air of Madrid can kill a man without blowing out a candle.* Certainly there is some truth in it but you must remember, dear Anita, that English women do not feel the cold. They are accustomed to it, their own climate – that is to say the climate of their native land – being, generally speaking, so inclement."

He was back on his old hobbyhorse and I was in no mood to put up with it.

"I know, I know," I said angrily, "Hardy Weeds can weather any amount of cold, unlike delicate blossoms, of course. They stand up to storms, they can be trampled underfoot – you can do anything to a Hardy Weed and it will bounce right back because it doesn't have any feelings, you know!"

Anita disentangled herself from Desmond and came over to where I was sitting. She put a hand on my shoulder and peered at me anxiously. "Whatever's the matter? This isn't like you at all. Something's upset you. In fact..." she examined me closer, "I think you've been crying. What's happened? Why are you sitting here brooding all by yourself?"

"I'm not brooding. Leave me alone!" I snapped, turning away from her.

"You are in a bad mood! That's what comes of being on your own. It's not good for you. Let's go and ring Rafael."

Desmond cleared his throat. "Unaware as I am of the exact nature or cause of her discomposure, it is, of course, difficult for me to comment, but on the other hand, I would venture to suggest that, from a general observation of her appearance and manner, she would appear to be suffering from a considerable degree of nervous tension. In such cases, a change of atmosphere is often considered beneficial and I would therefore recommend that we make immediate arrangements for an excursion into the mountains for the purpose of ski-ing and inhaling the fresh health-giving air."

If he'd said that in English, I thought, it would have sounded like an excerpt from a Wodehouse novel: Jeeves advising Bertie Wooster.

"Oh! What a wonderful idea!" exclaimed Anita, "I've never been ski-ing. Tomorrow's Sunday. We could go tomorrow. What do you think? Shall we ring Rafael and tell him? Or, better still, we could invite José Luis to join us. Yes, that's a better idea. He's sure to cheer you up."

I smiled, amused at her unshakeable faith in José Luis as a remedy for all ills.

"Neither of them," I said. "I have someone else in mind. Someone who is a great skier."

"Who's that?" she asked, intrigued.

"Oh, just another friend of mine. Chap called Daniel. I met him at a party last year when I was here and I know he's a good skier because he told me he goes up into the mountains every Sunday in the winter. He's mad about ski-ing so he'll probably make a good instructor."

"How many more friends do you have in Madrid?" laughed Anita. "Come on! Let's ring him now!"

ᘓ ᘔ

The mountain railway took us to a point close to the ski resort of Navacerrada but the rest of the journey had to be made on foot. It was hard going, encumbered as we were with our skis, and our upward trudge through the snow was not made any easier by the fact that both Anita and I were wearing trousers and ski boots belonging to the men, which were several sizes too large for us. We had tried to pad out the boots with assorted socks originating from both Desmond and Daniel but they only succeeded in making our feet feel even worse. They were heavy, bulky and clumsy. However, they did keep out the cold very effectively, as did the thick sweater that Daniel had lent me. The sun was shining and the snow glittered brightly under a clear blue sky. All around were pine trees, their branches powdered with snow and, here and there, tiny delicate crocuses pushed their mauve heads bravely through the white carpet, reminding us that spring was not too far away.

Desmond and Anita were way ahead of us, deep in conversation as usual, but this time I wasn't left alone. All my depression of the previous day was forgotten because I was with Daniel, one of my favourite friends. Kind and generous to a fault, he was utterly unaware of his own good looks and charm – the complete opposite of José Luis. Like most of the other people I'd met in Madrid, I had come to know him through my English friend, David, who patronised the family's small grocery business. It was tucked away down a back street in one of the less salubrious districts of the city and there, in his father's dark little shop, Daniel worked long and exhausting hours and Sunday being his only day off, he made good use of it to indulge in his two favourite interests: ski-ing and bullfighting.

I recalled my first experience of the National Fiesta that previous year when he had dragged me reluctantly to a bullfight. Having spent his week's hard-earned wages on two of the best seats in the shade, I could hardly tell him that the thought of spending two hours watching six great beasts being ritually tortured to death in a particularly barbarous and messy way, was not my idea of a pleasant Sunday afternoon's entertainment. In fact, my built-in revulsion for such things would have been totally incomprehensible to Daniel. At the time, I had some difficulty in reconciling his amiable nature with this apparently insatiable lust for blood. It was only after getting to know the Spanish character better, with its obsessive curiosity about the mystery of death, that I began to understand it.

I do not know who had suffered more that hot afternoon, the bulls or me. Daniel did his best to assuage my anguish by pointing out the various *pases* or movements of the cloak. By the end of the afternoon I had learned the difference between a *pase natural*, a *verónica* and a *mariposa*; but the most vivid image left in my mind was that of a once proud, beautiful and powerful animal staggering, bemused, around the ring, vomiting its life blood onto the sand with half a sword protruding grotesquely between its shoulders. The most frightening thing about that afternoon was that after being forced to witness the deaths of six bulls and the wounding of a horse, a picador and an *espontáneo* (a member of the public who had climbed into the ring to try his luck), I had become almost immune to the sight of blood and its accompanying dramas. I wondered whether this sinister desensitising process might occur among soldiers in the battlefield. Certainly, from observing Daniel's reactions, it was clear that to him the bull was not a suffering creature made of flesh and blood with nerves and feelings and a will to live, but merely a means by which the bullfighter could test and measure his own skill and valour.

When we'd left the ring Daniel had been decidedly depressed. It had not been a good bullfight he assured me. It was the first of the season and the *toreros* were not in good form so I should not judge all bullfights by this one. He would take me to others that would be better. However, I had promised myself never to take him up on this offer.

Now, as we wended our way up through the pine trees, weighed down by our skis, I reminded him of that distant April afternoon and he laughed. "That was a terrible *corrida*! I felt ashamed at having taken you to such a spectacle. Come back to Madrid this summer and I'll show you what bullfighting is really about!"

"I think I shall go home in the summer. I can't stay here indefinitely. But, talking of bullfighting, I know another madman like you, an *aficionado* called Felipe who lives in Burgos. You two should meet some time – you'd get on so well."

"I do have other interests," Daniel assured me, putting an arm round me. "We can talk of other things, you know, like how well you're looking; Spain really suits you, and what fun I'm going to have teaching you to ski!"

"You know, Daniel," I said gratefully, "you really are a good friend."

"*Señorita*," he responded, "if we were not both wearing such thick gloves, I would kiss your hand."

I smiled. In Daniel I felt I had someone resembling an older brother in whom I could, to some extent, confide.

"I've been a bit depressed lately," I confessed. "But being here with you is a real tonic."

Daniel looked surprised. "Why depressed? I can't imagine you depressed. What's the matter? Aren't you happy here in Spain? Are you homesick for England?"

"No, nothing like that. It's just that there have been ups and downs in my life lately and now happens to be one of the downs."

"I see. A personal matter?"

"Maybe."

"Someone has made you unhappy, perhaps?" he suggested with insight.

I nodded and turned away, feeling a fresh surge of misery. Daniel squeezed my shoulder. "Forget him!" he said in the softest of voices. "Forget him, whoever he is. No one should be allowed to take away your *alegría*. No one in the world."

"Dearest Daniel, if only it were that easy! If only life weren't so complicated."

"Those two don't seem to be having any problems, anyway," observed my companion, indicating the ever-diminishing figures of Desmond and Anita.

"That's another thing that bothers me. My best friend's got herself tied up with someone totally unsuitable. Desmond's too old for her and, let's face it, he's a pedantic bore."

"But not to her, it seems."

"No. That's the worst part about it. She's becoming just like him, starting to quote obscure German philosophers and things. It's awful."

"So, you think they're in love?"

"Think? I *know* it! Completely besotted; the pair of them."

"Like goats?"

"Exactly like goats. What's to be done?"

"If you've ever been in love you'll know the answer to that one. Nothing. Absolutely nothing."

I bit my lip and remained silent.

"Anyway," he continued after a pause, "it's really not for you to say who's right for her. Supposing she thought the same about whoever it is you're so keen on?"

I gave a cynical laugh. "That's exactly the situation; but I don't care what she thinks."

Daniel threw me a mischievous grin. "What more is there to be said?" he concluded.

By this time we were nearing our destination. We could see the ski slopes and the clubhouse coming into view but we had lost Anita and Desmond among the straggle of other skiers making their way up. I doubted we would see them again for some time.

cs so

The ski-ing lessons consisted of me wobbling precariously at the top of a gentle slope while Daniel stood at the bottom, arms spread wide, ready to catch me as I hurtled down towards him, clumsy, uncontrolled and weaving an erratic course which usually ended up with both of us rolling in the snow. Poor Daniel spent the best part of that day teaching me the rudiments of his favourite sport with patience and good humour.

In the middle of the afternoon I persuaded him to drop the lessons and enjoy himself for a bit on the steep slope where all the experts were showing off their skills. I stood among the pine trees watching as the ski lift carried him up and away. It was not long before I spotted his red sweater among the other skiers and was amazed by what I saw. There was Daniel, skimming effortlessly over the snow, weaving in and out of trees at frightening speed. He was no longer the grocer's son; it seemed to me that his skill had transformed him into some sort of super-being!

When he eventually glided over to me, his face flushed with cold and exhilaration, I felt compelled to embrace this amazing creature and flung my arms round his waist.

"You were wonderful! So clever! I've never seen anything like it!"

He laughed. "Nonsense! Most of these others are much better than me. Come on! Let's get back to the clubhouse. The sun's going down, it's getting cold and we need a drink."

We packed up our skis and set off towards the ski centre, hand-in-hand and in silence save for the crunch of snow beneath our boots and the sound of Daniel whistling softly, his breath drifting on the frosty air. Behind us, the sun had turned into a blood-red orb, casting a rosy glow over the snow, bathing everything in its incandescent light while our bodies cast long shadows ahead of us, like guides leading the way. I felt happy and at peace with the world and I wished this feeling could last forever.

Back at the clubhouse, a cheerful fire was blazing on the great stone hearth and round it, the skiers were gathered, drinking *anís* and thawing out. The room was buzzing with animated chatter as people joked and recounted the day's events. Desmond and Anita were nowhere to be seen.

Daniel ordered us a substantial *merienda*, for the cold and exercise had given us both healthy appetites. We sat down at a table near the door, warming our hands on the great steaming cups of coffee and watching out for Anita and Desmond.

We finished our meal and played four games of cards. Night had fallen, many of the skiers left for home but still there was no sign of the others. I began to feel worried. What if they had fallen into a crevasse or been buried in a snowdrift? My anxiety mounted despite soothing words from Daniel. I was just on the point of getting up to try and organize a search party when the two of them appeared through the door, locked in an embrace and still gazing at each other as though time had stood still for them.

I jumped up relieved and annoyed at the same time. "Where on earth have you two been all day?" I exploded.

Desmond turned his bearded face in my direction and regarded me in a supercilious manner. "I was not aware that we were obliged to account to you for our movements," he observed sarcastically.

"I was worried about you," I said to Anita, ignoring him, "we thought you might have got lost or had an accident."

"*Que tonta!* How silly!" smiled Anita coming over and sitting down beside me. "Of course we wouldn't get lost. We've had a wonderful afternoon, haven't we Desmond?"

She stretched her hand out to him and he pressed it to his lips before sitting down beside her. "Sweet Angel of Beauty," he droned, "words alone cannot adequately describe the bliss and solace of these golden hours we have spent together. Up here, in the pure, unadulterated mountain air, we have found the opportunity to look at ourselves afresh, examine our souls, consider our lives at this, their most important turning point." Here he paused, significantly looking at Anita who sighed happily and put her head on his shoulder. "We have, at last," he continued, "turned the key to unlock that inestimable treasure chest which is our mutual destiny."

"Oh, Desmond!" smiled Anita. "You have such a beautiful way of expressing things!"

All this sounded extremely ominous. I glanced at Daniel who looked amused.

"Have you been ski-ing?" he enquired innocently.

Desmond transferred his heavy-lidded eyes from Anita to Daniel. "Ski-ing?" he repeated incredulously. "Ski-ing? Do you imagine we would fritter away these precious moments in such idle activity? Indeed we have not. Our time has been most profitably spent in admiring the beauties of nature and marvelling at the complexity and diversity of those gifts with which God — or, if you like, The Ultimate Reality, has endowed this earth."

"Actually, we've been for a walk," explained Anita. "A beautiful, romantic walk."

I reminded Desmond that it had been his idea in the first place that we should go ski-ing and he who had supplied us with the gear, so Daniel's question was not unreasonable, but he ignored me.

"Well, anyway," said Daniel, "you'd better order something to eat and then we must be on our way back. Are you hungry? Let me get you something."

"Thank you, but that will not be necessary," replied Desmond. "We did, in fact, return briefly to the clubhouse for a little light refreshment while you were still out on the slopes."

"No, we're not at all hungry," confirmed Anita.

"When the soul is so well-nourished there is little need for physical sustenance," observed Desmond.

Under a clear starry sky, we made our way down to the mountain railway. The pine trees were basking in moonlight making them appear silvery and mysterious. It was a magical sight. Desmond was busy pointing out to Anita all the different stars, telling her their names and explaining their formations while she hung, spellbound, on his every word.

"Oh, how beautiful it all is!" she sighed. "How lovely it is up here! I wish we could stay here forever; and I am so happy! I have never felt so happy; except..." her face clouded a little, "except when I think about tomorrow."

"Why yes," I said cheerfully, "of course! We're going back to Burgos."

Desmond turned to Anita. "Do not let the thought of our imminent parting disturb you unduly, Precious Goddess, for I can assure you without a shadow of doubt that our separation shall not be of great duration."

"Well, well," commented Daniel when the others were out of earshot, "I see what you mean. He's the strangest man I've ever met and they really *are* like goats."

"It's dreadful," I groaned, "and getting worse all the time. Is there really nothing that can be done?"

Daniel put a comforting hand on my shoulder. "As I told you before: absolutely nothing. They're obviously deeply involved. I never saw such a devoted pair of *novios*."

"Oh! I suppose they are *novios*. I'd never thought of them that way. I hoped it was just a passing fancy on her part. I never really thought of them as serious *novios*."

"In that case," said my friend as we came out of the darkness into the station and joined the flock of day-trippers waiting on the platform with their gear, "in that case I think it's about time you got used to the idea."

CHAPTER TWENTY-ONE

THE WEEKEND OF SAN JOSÉ

Nothing had changed in Burgos since our departure a fortnight earlier. We arrived at the same bleak, dark hour of the morning as when we had left and emerged into the bitter cold, to find the Hotel España's battered old bus waiting for us in the snowy forecourt like a faithful servant.

Later that day, gathered round the cosy *brasero*, we recounted to Aunt Domi a carefully edited version of our adventures. Anita had kept from her the fact that we were planning to travel to Andalusia so we only told her about Madrid. She was delighted to have us back and kept hugging us in turn. Before long the kitchen was filled with all the usual friends and neighbours anxious to hear what we had been up to during our absence. Many expressed surprise that we had dared to travel alone – two young unaccompanied *señoritas* – and there were several raised eyebrows. What, we wondered, would have been their reaction had they known the whole story? What would they have thought about our drunken serenade in Jerez or the gory brawl in Seville? These things I could happily recount in my letters to my mother, but from Aunt Domi they had to be kept at all costs!

Having spent all the money I had saved, I had to get back to work at once. Although my mother had lent me money for the return journey to England, I had banked it in the hope that I would not have to use it except in an emergency, so now I had to save hard.

My pupils were pleased to resume their lessons, particularly the daughters of the Captain General who appeared to have missed me greatly and greeted me like a long-lost sister with affectionate kisses. As soon as I was able, I went to seek out Don Federico as I was anxious to resume my typing lessons. I tracked him down in his academy sorting through some papers. He was wearing his thick overcoat with the collar turned up against the chilly gloom and smoking a self-rolled cigarette, sprinkling his papers with its ash. The room was dark and I was surprised that he could still see what he was doing by the dim, fading light of that grey afternoon. I stood by the door and switched on the light. He raised his head and blinked as the single bulb, hanging limply from the crumbling ceiling, filled the room with its unfriendly glare.

"Ah! you're back!" he exclaimed, removing the cigarette end from his mouth and coming over to greet me. "Back from your travels at last. Well, Burgos has not been the same without you. All my friends in the bars, they are asking where are you."

I rushed over to hug him. "It's great to be back! We've had a fantastic time, but it's so good to be back!"

"Yes, yes; let's go to see! Let us have a little *copa* to celebrate your return," he suggested, glad of an excuse to get back to the bars. "I just tidy up these papers and then we go."

I shivered. "It's freezing in here, Freddie. How on earth can you work in this cold? And it was dark too when I got here. You'll strain your eyes and give yourself another dose of 'flu if you're not careful."

"I tell you, I tell you before: I am not friends with Doña Flu. She has never visited me in my life. But come, we go now to the Bar Paloma where is warm and you will tell me what you have been doing."

Over countless glasses of white wine, I gave him an unedited account of our adventures which he found highly amusing. I told him about Anita and her unlikely new *novio*. "He pays her the most ridiculous compliments: tells her that she is like a goddess — that sort of thing."

"Ah, but a compliment is a beautiful thing," said Federico smiling up at the ceiling. "*Shall I compare thee to a summer's day?*"

"*Thou art more lovely and more temperate,*" I interrupted. "You see I know that one! *Rough winds do shake the darling buds of May —* we learnt it at school."

"Sonnet number eighteen," muttered Federico, slightly put out by my interference with his quotation. "Wonderful poet your Shakespeare! Is wonderful poet."

I decided the time had come to talk business while I was still sober enough to do so. "About my typing lessons, Freddie, I want to start again as soon as possible."

"Yes," he said, "I know. You can come any time; any time before lunch because he is not coming any more."

"Who?" I croaked, a strange hot and cold sensation creeping over me, knowing full well the answer.

"Your lover, of course. He is not coming. He has gone to Madrid."

"Don Federico! If you call him that once more, I promise I'll crown you with the nearest bottle! You're being really annoying!"

Federico shrugged his shoulders, totally unruffled by my outburst. "He was asking me about you. Before he went he was asking me where were you."

"I'm not interested in him," I lied, draining my glass. "I don't want to hear anything about him. There's nothing between us anymore. He means *nothing* to me now. Can you understand that?"

Federico smiled indulgently and lit a cigarette. "Okay, If you say so, Baby. But then, I ask myself why are you so cross? *The lady doth protest too much methinks!* Hamlet, Act three, Scene two."

"Look Freddie," I said, trying to suppress my irritation, "I know I can't compete with you when it comes to Shakespeare quotations, but I do seem to remember something about *I come to bury Caesar, not to praise him* and I don't know the exact reference, but could we please apply that particular saying to the subject in question?"

Federico nodded and rapped on the counter to call the attention of the barman. "Julius Caesar," he murmured absently, chewing on his cigarette, "and that also is Act three, Scene two."

CB BO

The end of February saw the snow beginning to melt, turning to icy rain or sleet but the weather was still extremely cold. The house was again beginning to fill with relatives. Anita's cousin, Margarita, had come over to see her boyfriend, Jacinto, something she did as often as feasible given the distance she had to travel from France. It was good to have her there as her lively presence always lifted the spirits of those around her.

The harshness of that winter was considerably softened for Anita by the daily arrival of Desmond's love letters which appeared, regular as clockwork, each morning on the breakfast table and which she read with the utmost rapture.

Over my cup of coffee, I would watch her savouring each page – and there were many – to the accompaniment of sighs and little giggles of delight. Occasionally, she would read me odd extracts.

"Listen to this! *The flame of love which you, adored Light of my Life, have kindled in my heart shall burn for ever like an inextinguishable fire melting the ice which sorrow at our parting has cast upon my soul. It gives me strength to endure that indescribable agony which this doleful absence from you has inflicted upon me. Oh! That my spirit could take wings to span the paltry distance which divides us, that these two kindred souls of ours, having so fortuitously found each other while wandering through the wilderness that we call this earthly life, should once more be united as it has no doubt been ordained by Divine Providence...* Isn't that wonderful? What other man could write such things?"

In addition to writing her daily letters, Desmond had promised her that he would travel to Burgos as often as possible. I realised that I would have to take Daniel's advice and resign myself to the fact that they were now definitely *novios*.

One day, alongside Anita's three letters from Desmond which had accumulated over a weekend, I found one for me, post-marked Logroño. From this and the familiar writing on the envelope, I knew at once that it was from Julio.

'*I was in Burgos a few weeks ago and you weren't there*' it began accusingly. '*I took several days off from all the pressing business I have in hand at the moment only to be told by various people that you were gallivanting all over Spain. What will you think of next? Why did you not tell me of your intentions so that I could accompany you? I hear you were in Madrid again and I don't trust you in Madrid. Not after last* spring. *And if I find out that you've been flirting with that Rafael again, I shall deal with him once and for all the next time I am there on business. I don't trust anyone with my niña. As you know, the important project I am working on at present takes me frequently to Madrid so it would be a simple matter to look him up and get to the truth of all this. It is hard work trying to keep track of you here in Spain. It wasn't like this when you were in London. In England you stayed in one place, lived in the same house. I always knew where to find you. There was none of this flitting around from place to place. Anyway, the purpose of this letter is to let you know that, despite my recent wasted journey, I shall again try to see you this coming weekend. I have to see someone in Valladolid next Monday so I shall take the opportunity of stopping over in Burgos. Preoccupied as I am with important matters concerning my business and valuable as is every minute of my time, as you well know, I shall expect, this time, to find my niña where she should be.'*

"What are you reading? Who's it from?" asked Anita nosily, looking up from her own letter.

"I've been summoned by Julio to meet him on Sunday."

"I don't know how you can stand going out with him. He's so bossy and conceited."

"Not as conceited as Desmond," I retorted, stuffing Julio's letter into my coat pocket and winding a scarf round my neck in preparation for my battle with the elements.

"Well, at least Desmond's got something to be conceited about. Oh, and by the way, you're not the only one with a date this weekend. Desmond's coming all the way up from Madrid just to see me, like he promised. I'm so happy and excited!"

Margarita was prancing around the kitchen putting away newly-washed dishes from the night before's supper. She stopped to look at us with her hands on her hips.

"*Ay! Ay! Ay!*" she exclaimed. "You two girls have all the luck! Devoted admirers travelling from all corners of Spain to be with you! But how about me? Jacinto just sits pretty and I'm the one who has to do all the running: all the way from France too!"

"And that's good news," I remarked. "If it weren't that way round, we'd never get the chance to see you."

Margarita grinned and poured me a generous glass of anís.

Anita stretched herself and yawned. "I think it's time I started looking for a job. In fact, I could have had one last week. I forgot to tell you I met old Vázquez in the street and he offered to take me back; said he couldn't manage without me."

"I take it you didn't agree?" I ventured.

"Agree? Wild horses wouldn't drag me back within reach of those groping hands!"

☙ ❧

The following Sunday brought a change in the weather. The morning was bright and sunny although there was still a keen wind. Anita had left the house in the small hours to meet Desmond off the train and I hadn't seen her since.

As I entered the Plaza Mayor on my way to find Julio, I came across blind Emilio standing on his usual corner, a string of lottery tickets pinned to his ragged coat. He was leaning against the wall, his haggard, sightless face raised to receive the unfamiliar warmth of the February sun. I saw that he was alone and, without his son to inform him, was unaware of my approach.

He started when I touched his arm. "Emilio!" I said. "Hello, it's me. I've come for my ticket."

His face broke into a delighted smile. "The English *señorita*!" He fumbled to tear off one of the tickets. "*Buenos días, buenos días,* how are you today? Are you happy?"

"Why, yes," I replied in some surprise.

"That is good." He clasped my hand as I gave him the money. "My son tells me that the English *señorita* has not been looking very happy just lately."

"I'm fine, really. But how about you? Are you well?"

"I am the better for seeing you. Did you hear what I said? *Seeing* you! Of course, I cannot see you but I hear your voice and that is sufficient. I know you have a kind heart and God will grant you a happy life."

"Where's your son today?"

The smile faded from his gaunt face. "He cannot come out today. He is too ill."

226

"That's bad news," I said, putting my arm round him. "And I'm sorry. Is it the cough?"

Emilio nodded gravely and I felt worried. Judging from the boy's pallor and emaciated appearance together with his constant dry cough, I suspected he might be suffering from tuberculosis. It was frightening to realise just how prevalent this dreadful disease still was in Spain.

"I must go," I said. "I have to meet a friend but give my love to Paco and wish him better for me."

My meeting with Emilio had delayed me and when I arrived at the café where I had arranged to meet Julio, I found him already there, pacing to and fro impatiently. When he saw me he darted forward, grabbing me by the arm.

"You're late!" he snapped, glancing pointedly at his watch. "More than ten minutes late. In London you would have arrived on time. You are getting into such bad Spanish habits."

"Yes, I'm sorry. It's just that I met a friend on the way..."

"Excuses! Well, never mind, the important thing is that you are here and not in Andalusia or Galicia or Cataluña or wherever."

"Stop nagging!" I laughed, pushing him towards the café. "I can't think why you resent me having a holiday. It was fantastic. We had so many adventures."

"What kind of adventures?" a note of suspicion crept into his voice.

"Well, we met a rich American who took us half way round Andalusia in his posh car. Then we were serenaded in Jerez by a drunken flamenco singer; oh! – and in Seville, two men came to blows over Anita and nearly killed each other."

Julio ran his fingers through his unruly hair and rolled his eyes in despair. "I knew it! I knew you'd get up to that sort of thing the minute you were out of my sight. I should appoint a permanent guard to keep an eye on you all the time when I'm away."

"Why?"

He caught my hand under the table and crushed it painfully. "Because you are my English *niña*!" he hissed between clenched teeth. "And I'm responsible for you while you're in Spain. I promised your mother I would look after you, see that you came to no harm, and what happens? The minute my back is turned you are off on some crazy escapade."

I straightened his crooked tie. "Stop being so stuffy and old-fashioned! I would have thought having lived in England, you would have known better. We British girls are completely emancipated and we don't need chaperons, thank you. We're quite capable of looking after ourselves."

Julio turned his attention to his coffee cup, stirring it sulkily and frowning.

"How's the business going?" I asked, keen to steer the conversation away from the subject of my independence.

At the mention of his business he brightened, pulling from the inside pocket of his jacket, a wad of crumpled papers which he spread across the table. They appeared to be scribbled lists of names and addresses.

"Look!" he said, thumbing through them, "These are all the contacts I have made since I last saw you, all the people who are interested in my project. It is very encouraging. Everything is going according to plan. This time I shall be successful. My bank manager has been very helpful. He understands my position; sees all the possibilities. Yes, this is going to be a success and you will be pleased that you are my *niña*. All your friends will be jealous that you are the *novia* of Julio Rivera."

He looked so earnest and excited – like a child talking about a new toy, that I could not stop myself from laughing and ended up choking over my coffee. Julio stopped talking and stared at me, disconcerted and surprised. "Why are you laughing? You are always laughing at me. Why don't you take these matters seriously?"

I controlled my laughter with some difficulty. "Oh, but I do," I assured him soothingly. "Of course I do and I'm pleased your project's going well."

"Well? That's an understatement. You'd be amazed if you fully realised what I'm undertaking, if you understood what it all implies. I'm planning to start manufacturing in the very near future: first in Logroño and later in Madrid. Everything has been worked out on a sound financial basis. This time I can't go wrong."

After listening for another half hour about his business, I suggested we went for a walk during which I managed to move the conversation on to Eduardo.

"How is he? I haven't seen him in ages. He usually calls when he's passing through Burgos."

"The idiot's put himself in hospital again. It was just before Christmas and he was playing football. Can you imagine? Playing *football*? Just asking for trouble. Anyway, he fell over and sprained something and that put him in hospital for weeks. In fact, he's only just come out. His family were beside themselves with worry."

"If only he'd be more careful," I sighed. "Poor Eduardo!"

"Poor Eduardo! Poor Eduardo! That's what everyone says but he's no one but himself to blame. He hasn't a scrap of common sense and just goes around pretending he's normal and making life impossible for everyone else. I've no patience with him. I'm fed to the teeth with him."

"You're always so harsh. Why don't you try to see things from his point of view? How would you like it if you had a horrible condition like that and you knew there was no cure and it restricted your life all the time? I bet you'd feel like rebelling: feel like saying to hell with all this, I'll do what I want to do and hope for the best."

"Bah! You're always defending him. Nothing can alter the fact that he's a fool and always has been. He'll end up killing himself sooner or later."

We stopped at the cinema and tried to get tickets for the evening showing but they had sold out. I suggested the Sala de Fiestas instead but Julio said he didn't like dancing. "I don't need any artificial entertainment when I'm with my *niña*," he said.

 C⅜ ℬ

I saw Anita and Desmond once that day, walking in the Espolón. They were so engrossed in conversation that they didn't even notice us and I let them pass by with some relief.

Night fell and Julio said he was feeling hungry and that he planned to take me for a meal, a really good meal as befitted his role as a successful businessman.

"I've been making a few enquiries," he said. "And I understand there are several good eating places round here but the best one, so I've been told, is across the river there. Now, what did they say its name was? Let me think! ... La Gitana? No, that's not right. It was something odd – like the name of a woman. La... La... La Morena! That's it! Restaurante La Morena. We'll go there."

I felt a chill down my spine. Paco's mother's place! Paco, Luis's best friend, would be there.

"No," I protested, "honestly, Julio, it's not that good. I hear it's not as good as it was."

"Nonsense! I've heard excellent reports of it. It's got a fine reputation and they say La Morena is a first class cook. The man at the station was telling me all about it. Yes, I've made up my mind. We'll go there."

"But I'm not all that hungry," I lied in desperation, inwardly cursing the good reputation of Paco's establishment. "I couldn't do justice to one of their enormous meals. All this heavy Castilian cooking is ruining my figure as it is. If only we were back in London! How I long for one of those simple meals we used to have at Lyon's Corner House!"

To my relief, the mention of London had the desired effect. "Ah yes! London!" his eyes glazed with nostalgia. "Steak and kidney pudding with two veg. Fish and chips!"

"Apple pie and custard?" I suggested. "Roast beef and Yorkshire pud?"

He turned to look at me, eyes softening with affection. "Of course, there's nothing here that can compare with British cookery. Nothing here compares with London. Take transport, for example..."

"I have an idea!" I interrupted brightly. "Why don't we try the Hotel España? They serve international cuisine because all the foreigners go there – you know, business men, those sort of people." Happily, Julio readily agreed.

Our dinner at the Hotel España was excellent and so was the wine. Julio ordered Rioja which came from his native region and was, according to him, the only wine worth drinking. He consumed it in considerable quantity and I knew, from experience, what effect it would have on him and prepared myself for the struggle that lay ahead.

"I shall walk with you back to your house before I catch my train," he informed me ominously as he fixed me with a steady gaze across the table, his dark eyes narrowing, seething with unconcealed desire. After what seemed an age, he turned away and clapped his hands in an imperious manner. "Waiter!" he called. "Bring the bill!"

The streets were quiet and dark as we walked back towards Anita's house. Suddenly, but predictably, he pushed me into a doorway in his usual caveman style, smothering me with fierce kisses with never a pause for breath and crushing me against the wall in a passionate, suffocating embrace. I struggled to free myself, wondering what his feelings for me really were for in all the time we had known each other he had never once told me he loved me.

"Julio!" I choked, gasping for breath, "You had better stop this! You know what it's like here. If a policeman were to walk by right now, he'd have us both arrested for immoral behaviour."

He stared at me in surprise. "What's the matter?" he demanded breathlessly, "you weren't like this in London. Are you turning into a Spanish prude? All this talk of policemen! You didn't worry about policemen in London. You didn't worry about policemen in Hyde Park!"

"Because everything's different back home. Have you forgotten this is a Police State with some very funny ideas? You can get arrested for the slightest thing: like kissing in public or wearing a bikini."

"You wait till I get you back to London!" he hissed. "I'll show you how a Spaniard can make love!"

"Oh, I see. So you're a Spaniard when you're a lover but an Englishman when it comes to setting up a business. Is that right?"

"You're making fun of me again."

At that moment there was the sound of voices and I made a further effort to disentangle myself, but to no avail. A group of chattering youngsters passed our doorway and, to my horror, I realised they were my group of friends. I hoped they wouldn't notice us but then I heard Mari Carmen's voice, high and piercing. "*Hola!* I thought it was you. What are you doing? Come and join us!"

Julio released me hastily and straightened his tartan tie while I smoothed down my dishevelled hair, trying not to look too embarrassed. "Oh, hello you lot," I smiled awkwardly. "This is a friend of mine, Julio."

Julio shook hands with them curtly, muttering *mucho gusto* and looking thoroughly annoyed at being disturbed.

"Come and have a drink with us!" invited Felipe. "That's if you're not in a hurry."

"Or have better things to do!" added Mari Carmen with a facetious titter.

"I'm on my way home," I replied in some confusion, "and Julio has to catch a train so we'd better say no."

"Never mind," said Mari Carmen. "We'll walk back with you and you can tell us all about that fabulous Andalusian holiday of yours."

Julio glared at them angrily then he looked at his watch and said: "I'd better leave you here or I shall miss my train. *Adios.* I shall be in touch."

He turned and walked briskly away. "Julio!" I called after him but he ignored me and disappeared round the corner.

"Well! well!" giggled Mari Carmen. "You foreign girls certainly ring the changes! First that boy Luis, then the one we met in the Sala de Fiestas and now this one! I wish we Spanish girls were as enterprising!"

ⓒ ⓑ

The little *automotor* gave a tuneful hoot as it swung round between the rocks, following the twisting River Ebro through a mountainous landscape, spring-like and beautiful, spangled with blossoming almond and apricot. Coming down into the Ebro Valley from the bleak meseta was like entering a different world. It was well worth the troublesome journey: catching first the Irún express as far as Miranda de Ebro where I had to endure a two hour wait in the cold before boarding the *automotor*, a fast new diesel train carrying second class only. It was the weekend of San José, a public holiday, and I was on my way to Logroño at the invitation of Eduardo.

Only a day or so after Julio's visit, I received a letter from Eduardo. It was a cheerful, chatty letter, with never a mention of his recent spell in hospital. He urged me to take up the invitation he had offered me the previous autumn to stay with him in Logroño for a long weekend. He wrote: '*My family's anxious to meet you and you are very welcome to stay at our house. How about next weekend which is San José? It would be a great opportunity and I can't wait to see Julio's face when you arrive! I shan't say a thing about it until the last minute. I know he regards you as his personal property and it will be really funny to see his reaction. Do say you can come!*'

I knew his mischievous proposal had quite a lot to do with getting even with his friend for various past grievances, but I enjoyed Eduardo's company and welcomed the chance to see Logroño so I wrote back at once, accepting. After all, if Julio had wanted me to stay with him, he could equally well have invited me.

I looked out of the window. The bright sunshine, which had flooded the carriage all afternoon, mellowed as evening approached and soon a fiery sky blazed behind the peaks, turning the river a shimmering red. Entranced, I watched the colours fade as the sky darkened, till all that was left of the sunset were a few fluffy, pink clouds floating across the mountains and the river changed again, to a snaking streak of silver. As night enveloped us, the twinkling lights of Logroño came into sight, nestling in the valley.

Julio, Eduardo and Eduardo's sister were waiting for me at the station. Eduardo was smiling cheerfully, but I noticed that he looked a little pale, and as he walked over to greet me, he appeared to be limping slightly. He relieved me of my suitcase and introduced me to his sister, Mari Paz. She was a slight girl with a pretty, round face and a smile just like her brother's. She embraced me warmly, giving me the traditional kiss on both cheeks.

Julio did not welcome me. He was standing slightly apart, arms folded and frowning, with a face of thunder.

"Hello Julio!" I said, waving to him. "Isn't this nice? I never thought I'd be seeing you again so soon."

Julio muttered something inaudible and Eduardo gave me a wink. "Come on!" he said. "My car's here. I'll drive you straight to our house, you can drop your things off there and then there'll be time for us to show you a bit of the town before supper."

We piled into Eduardo's tiny car. Julio opened the rear door for Mari Paz and then climbed in beside her while I sat in the front next to Eduardo.

"Did you know Eduardo had such a beautiful sister?" asked Julio, putting his arm round her.

I glanced at Eduardo and saw that it was all he could do to stifle his laughter. "I've another one equally *guapa* at home but she couldn't come. She's helping with the cooking," he said.

"When it comes to real beauty," said Julio, "there are few girls who can match Mari Paz."

"Well, thank you, Julio," said the girl, sounding surprised. "It's nice of you to say that but I think you must be joking."

"I am not," he said, his voice deadly serious, "I have travelled widely, as you know, and I know a beautiful girl when I see one."

"Julio!" laughed Mari Paz. "What is the matter with you? Have you been drinking?"

"Too much Rioja, that's what it is," said Eduardo with another wink. "It always turns him into a Don Juan."

Julio leaned forward angrily. "Don't be ridiculous! You think I don't mean what I say? I never say anything I don't mean and if I say Mari Paz is beautiful then that is exactly what I mean. Mari Paz is beautiful. Do you all hear me?"

I turned round to look at him. He was becoming increasingly agitated, his eyes flashing furiously. Mari Paz blushed and covered her face with her hands in embarrassment. I put my hand on Julio's wrist. "We're only joking," I said.

He snatched his hand away like a sulky child and sank back in his seat, staring moodily out of the window.

"Take no notice of him! He's being stupid," said Mari Paz.

We arrived at a large house on the outskirts of the town. Eduardo's father, round and jovial, was at the gate to meet us.

"So this is the English girl we've heard so much about? Welcome to Logroño! Come on in, you must be in need of some refreshment after that long journey."

Meeting his family made me understand why Eduardo was such a likeable person. His home was full of warmth and affection and the family went to enormous pains to make me feel welcome. It was obvious that they were of comfortable means. The house was large and stood on its own surrounded by a blossoming orchard. So pleasant were the members of Eduardo's family that I persuaded him to postpone our tour of Logroño until the following day, preferring to stay and talk to them. Julio announced that he couldn't possibly spare any more of his valuable time to be with us that evening as he had several important business letters to write and with this he departed in a huff.

Eduardo's family was deeply religious as was clear from the abundance of crucifixes, statuettes of Christ displaying His Sacred Heart and paintings of the Virgin which adorned the house. In my white-walled room hung a magnificent reproduction of The Immaculate Conception by Zurbarán. Julio had told me that it was their faith that had sustained them during the numerous crises they had suffered in the course of bringing up Eduardo and, without it, doubtless all of them would have ended up as nervous wrecks.

ᘓ ᘔ

When I awoke the next morning and pushed back the shutters, a welcome stream of warm sunshine poured into the room. The sky was a cloudless blue and birds were singing in the orchard. Exhilarated, I leaned out of the window, breathing in the fresh, fragrant air, revelling in the warm caress of the strengthening Spanish sun. Suddenly, it felt marvellous to be alive: to be young, healthy and on the threshold of a life which at that moment seemed full of promise. The cold Burgos winter, the agony of losing Luis, the uncertainty of my future, all those depressing things seemed to have melted away, banished by the enchantment of this glorious spring day. Then I heard a shout from below and there was Eduardo's cheerful face beaming up at me.

"Come on down!" he called. "I'll show you the garden."

We walked through long, damp grass sprinkled with daffodils, wending our way between fruit trees heavy with clusters of pink and white blossom. In one corner of the garden stood a large kennel with an enormous dog sprawled across its entrance. It rose to its feet as we approached and ambled towards us, languidly wagging its bushy tail.

"I'm sorry about last night," said Eduardo. "I mean about Julio being so rude and all that silly flirting with my sister. It was unforgivable."

"It didn't bother me in the least. I thought it was hilarious."

"He only did it to make you jealous. He's never shown the slightest interest in Mari Paz before."

"I'm really not bothered. Anyway, why shouldn't he be interested in Mari Paz? She's a very attractive girl."

"But it was all an act. He was absolutely furious when he found out you were coming to stay with me and now he's trying to annoy both of us."

"Well, we knew he wouldn't be very pleased, didn't we?"

"But I didn't think he'd take it this badly. He must be crazy about you."

"No! You know what he's like – full of that awful pride and honour thing you Spanish males are so obsessed with; I've seen it all before."

"How funny you should say that. He's always telling me how English he's becoming."

"Believe me, Eduardo, you couldn't find anyone less English in the whole wide world."

Eduardo laughed and bent to pat the dog which had decided to join us on our walk. "Well, I hope Julio's behaviour won't spoil your weekend in Logroño," he said.

"No chance of that! It's wonderful being here. The weather's good and I really like your family; and, as I said, I think Julio's right about Mari Paz. She's very pretty – both your sisters are – and I bet they've got tons of admirers."

Eduardo nodded. "They have; especially Mari Paz but of course she never encourages them because she'll never be able to marry."

"Why ever not?" I asked in amazement.

"Because… because of the curse of this family." He kicked angrily at a stone. "Because of this damned haemophilia."

"But you told me girls don't get it."

Eduardo raised his eyebrows in surprise. "Didn't you know? It's a genetic condition. Females don't suffer from it but they are the carriers who pass it down to the next generation of males. Neither of my sisters can marry and, for that matter, neither can I. Even If I marry someone who's normal, I could pass it down to my daughters, who in turn would become carriers." He gave a bitter laugh. "I suppose I shall have to enter the priesthood!"

"Oh, surely it can't be that bad! You could still marry if you both agreed not to have children."

Eduardo shook his head. "For us that's not an option. We're Catholics and I couldn't ask that of any woman. There's a girl I like. I like her very much but I dare not let myself fall in love with her. I couldn't offer her a normal life."

We had reached the end of the orchard and he stood still for a minute staring out across the fields towards the distant mountains. I said nothing. Perhaps I was beginning to understand why he took such risks with his health. He felt he had little to lose as he could only see before him a future of pain and frustration.

After a while he roused himself from his reverie and turned to me with a warm smile. "Never mind! There are other things in life to enjoy – like a good breakfast. Let's go back to the house, the coffee should be ready by now."

CR SO

Julio condescended to join us when we toured the town's bars later that morning but he was still in a sulk and took pains to ignore me completely, giving all his attention to Mari Paz who by this time was becoming a little bored with him. I was more than surprised therefore, when just before lunch he informed me that his family had invited me for *merienda* at his house that afternoon. He would call for me at five promptly and I was not to keep him waiting.

"I knew he couldn't keep it up for much longer!" joked Eduardo over lunch. "And now you're going to meet his family. That should be interesting."

On the dot of five Julio called for me. He was still disgruntled and as soon as we were alone together in the street, he grabbed me roughly by the arm and swung me round to face him.

"What do you mean by staying with Eduardo?" he demanded, fuming with indignation. "What are you doing there without consulting me? Why didn't you say anything about this when I saw you? Are you trying to make me look a fool? What's been going on behind my back? Is this the way to treat your *novio*?"

I pulled myself away from him crossly. "This sounds unpleasantly like an inquisition. We're not *novios* and I don't have to answer any of those questions."

"Because you can't! Because there's nothing you can say. You and Eduardo have planned this, haven't you? To make me look a fool. How do you think it looks for me when everyone knows my *novia's* staying here in Logroño in another man's house: in the house of my closest friend? *Hombre!*"

"I'm not your *novia*," I reminded him again gently, trying to keep my patience, "and even if I were, there would be nothing wrong in my staying with Eduardo. He's my friend as well as yours so stop trying to control my life! He invited me here for the weekend of San José so here I am. End of story."

He snatched at my arm and pulled me closer to him. "Just remember you're *my niña a*nd let's have no more of this eccentric behaviour! You give me nothing but trouble. First I come to Burgos to find you and you've moved house; then, the next time I come, you're not even there. No! You're roaming around Andalusia flirting with drunken flamenco singers. And now *this*! It's unbelievable. You should be more careful. Girls here never do things like that."

"Have you heard the song *Mad dogs and Englishmen go out in the midday sun*? Well, that equally applies to us females."

"But not to my girl. I don't like to think of my *niña* doing such things."

We had reached the centre of the town and stopped at a small hairdressers. Julio's mother was a widow who ran the business with her daughters. This much I already knew, but what I was not prepared for was that he had so many sisters. There were six of them and they were all waiting for us at the top of the stairs. They ushered us into their flat which was above the shop and I found myself in a large, dark room with a long table formally set with a white cloth. On it were a number of plates piled high with different kinds of cream cakes and biscuits.

Julio introduced me to his mother, a small, grey-haired woman, considerably older than I had expected, dressed in black with a woollen shawl draped about her shoulders. She greeted me politely and led me to the table, inviting me to sit next to her. One of the sisters brought wine and coffee and the *merienda* began. It all seemed rather odd, almost surreal. The mother sat at one end of the table and Julio at the other while all the sisters took their places on either side. I studied them with interest. They were all older than Julio – the oldest fast approaching middle-age – and they were all unmarried. Sitting there, very upright in high-backed chairs, all dressed in black, it was like stepping into a scene from one of Lorca's plays. It soon became obvious, as we conversed, that the one thing that united all these female members of the family was their unquestioning devotion to Julio and, for the first time, I understood the reason for his brash chauvinism and bossiness. As the youngest of seven children and the only son, (so long awaited after six daughters), he had been indulged since birth, adored by his mother and worshipped by his sisters. In his mother's home and in the absence of his father, he ruled the roost and he was the one who gave the orders as the head of the household.

"Why haven't you made tea?" he complained. "In London we always drink tea. This is an English girl you are entertaining."

"Prepare tea, Luisa!" ordered his mother and the sister next to me jumped to her feet. Fortunately, I managed to restrain her, remembering Señorita Alvárez's undrinkable brew. "Please don't make any on my account," I begged. "I'd really much prefer coffee."

The mother smiled indulgently. "Julio has acquired so many British habits," she said. "He is always telling me about life in London and it is all so interesting. Of course, we miss him a great deal when he is away, but we realise these journeys are necessary and he has made so many good friends there as well as learning the language so well. Don't you think he speaks good English?"

"Oh yes," I agreed, "very good."

"He has always been so good at languages, but then he is good at most things, is that not so, Julio?" Except business, I thought, and how to treat girls.

"Any friend of Julio's is more than welcome in this house," continued the mother. "Please feel free to come whenever you like."

"My sisters are very musical," said Julio. "Later they will play their instruments for you."

"I see you have a talented family," I said to the mother. "And you run your own business too. That must be hard work."

One of the sisters opposite patted her mouth with her napkin and said rather timidly, "If you would ever like a shampoo and set, we should be only too pleased to do that for you."

"Such pretty hair!" remarked the mother, leaning forward to touch my head. "Such a nice colour."

"Is it... natural?" one of the sisters asked hesitantly.

"Of course it's natural," interrupted Julio, helping himself to a cream cake. "English girls are naturally blonde. You should know that. They don't need all those bleaches and dyes your customers are so fond of."

I opened my mouth to refute this ludicrous assumption but failed to get a word in edgeways as Julio was off again on his favourite subject.

"You should *see* the women in London! Beautiful, blonde girls, tall as statues walking down Bond Street: high stilettos, straight seams, slim waists, full skirts – *hombre!* What elegance!" His eyes rolled ecstatically as he recalled these delectable images. "English women are amazing. Even their queen is beautiful. They're an incredible people altogether, the British. Thoroughly efficient. That's what I like about them. Even Hitler couldn't

240

destroy them. Swept through all the other countries in Europe but he couldn't beat the British. Why? Because they were *efficient!* Just a handful of their little Spitfires defeated the entire German Luftwaffe. That's efficiency for you. That's what we need here."

I felt tempted, at this point, to mention the Spanish Armada as I knew from experience that this would bring him rushing back to the defence of his own country. I decided, however, that this would not be tactful in front of the family.

The *merienda* over, Julio ordered his sisters to entertain me. "Luisa, bring your mouth organ! Dolores, play the accordion for our guest!"

Obediently, they hurried off to find their instruments and we settled down to hear what was obviously a well-rehearsed concert. Again, I experienced that strange feeling of unreality. It was such an odd scene. There we were in that old-fashioned gloomy room, Julio and I sitting either side of his venerable mother, two of his sisters performing in turn in the middle of the room while the others lined up stiffly in a row. Had the sisters been playing the piano rather than a mouth organ, we could have been in a nineteenth century drawing room.

When we eventually left the house to meet up with Eduardo and Mari Paz at the local cinema, Julio seemed in a much better mood. Gone were the sulks and he was even quite jovial.

"When I'm rich," he said, taking my hand, "when I'm rich and successful, as I soon shall be, my family will not have to slave away in that miserable little hairdressing place. No. I shall provide for them and they will have everything they need. Big house, a car, anything – anything they want. And it will be the same for the girl I choose to marry. Whoever I decide to marry will not want for anything." He gave my hand a squeeze. "Fur coats, French perfume, jewels; you'll see!"

"Lucky her!" I said, straightening his ever-crooked tie.

ങ ✼

As I hurried through the dark and windy streets of Burgos, I heard someone calling my name. I had decided to walk home from the station instead of taking the Hotel España's bus as my luggage was light and I needed time to collect my thoughts. This I had not been able to do during the train journey as I had met a family from Madrid who spoke English and were anxious to practise it all the way to Burgos. Now, at last I was alone and my thoughts were of Julio.

What was I to do about him? He refused to accept that we were not *novios* so how could I convince him without hurting his feelings too much? I was fond of him despite his many eccentricities (which I found rather amusing), but I knew he would never be right for me.

It was during these musings that I heard my name being called from somewhere behind me. I turned, and to my consternation, saw the tall figure of Paco, Él de La Morena striding towards me. This was the last person I wanted to see!

"Haven't seen you for ages," he said, catching me up. "Come and have a drink at my bar!"

"I can't. I'm in a hurry."

"Where are you going?"

"Home."

He relieved me of my bag. "Then I'll walk with you a little way. Girls shouldn't be out alone at night."

"Oh no!" I groaned. "Not you too!"

We walked on for a few minutes in silence and then he said: "I hear you've been away on holiday in Andalusia."

"Yes. That was in January. How did you know?"

"Federico told me. Luis has gone away too. Did you know that? He's gone back to study in Madrid."

I nodded. At the mention of Luis I felt again that sickening ache of misery which I had been trying so hard to suppress and I wished Paco would go away.

"But he came home for the weekend of San José. He's only just gone back."

"How... how is he?" I tried not to sound too interested.

"As well as can be expected in the circumstances."

I felt a sudden panic. Could he have suffered a relapse? Terrible visions crossed my mind: visions of Luis lying pale and wasted on his deathbed, coughing blood, perhaps murmuring my name in his fevered sleep. No! Of course not! It would be Maruja's name he would whisper as he tossed and turned in his delirium.

"What do you mean by 'as well as can be expected'? What's wrong with him? Is he ill again?"

Paco raised his eyebrows. "I'm surprised you're so concerned. Does it matter to you, then?"

"Of course it matters to me! Has he suffered a relapse?"

Paco gave a humourless laugh. "It's not his lungs that are the problem this time. It's his heart."

"Oh no! I never knew he had a weak heart too. Has he seen a doctor?"

Paco laughed again but this time genuinely. "I don't think a doctor could help. It's nothing physical. You know, it's strange. I've just come from seeing him off and just as he got onto the Madrid train, you stepped off it. Where have you been?"

"Logroño."

"Oh yes, Logroño, of course. Isn't that where your new boyfriend lives? Someone told me he was from Logroño. Have you had a nice weekend?"

Suddenly his voice was cold and sarcastic and I felt like bursting into tears. All I wanted, now that I knew Luis wasn't ill, was to get away from Paco but he continued to torment me.

"Luis has not been at all happy." I heard him say.

"I'm sorry to hear that. I thought he liked Madrid and enjoyed studying medicine."

"He does but..."

"Well, anyway," I interrupted bitterly, "if he has any problems at least he has Maruja to comfort him. At least he has *her*!" I swallowed hard.

Paco stopped walking and caught me by the arm. "Maruja?" he sounded surprised. "You mean the Institute gardener's daughter?"

"Who else?"

"But I thought you knew. Didn't you know?"

"Know what? For goodness sake, Paco, stop talking in riddles!"

"It's just... I thought Luis would have told you. It's all over between those two. Has been for some time. He broke it off with her months ago, soon after you told him about this what's-his-name? The one you're going around with now; that *novio* of yours from Logroño."

CHAPTER TWENTY-TWO

FAREWELL TO THE MIDDAY SUN

Spring came reluctantly to Burgos. April passed but still that relentless cold wind whistled across the *meseta*. The leaf buds on the trees in the Espolón remained obstinately closed and only unfurled themselves, grudgingly, in early May, forced on by the strengthening sun. During those spring months I threw myself enthusiastically into my work, slaving away for long hours with my pupils, drilling into them the difficult, inconsistent structure of my language and forcing their unwilling tongues to pronounce obscure Anglo-Saxon sounds. To this end I devised various unusual methods which, through trial and error, proved reasonably successful. One was to make them read English with a cigarette or pencil in their mouths, thus preventing them from using wide Spanish vowel sounds. I also confounded them with long lists of verbs based on the word "get" in combination with assorted prepositions and crammed them with all the possible abbreviations of the various tenses. I was determined that if they were to learn English at all, they would learn it properly. (For all this I was accused of being a hard task-master.) One of them, when struggling with the English short vowel sounds, suddenly turned on me in exasperation. "Don't you people ever get sore throats making such weird noises all day?" Nevertheless, my efforts bore fruit and I was well pleased with the progress they were all making.

All this hard work helped to keep my mind off troublesome thoughts about Luis. I had been greatly disturbed by what Paco had revealed and felt uncertain as to what I should do. Part of me, the sentimental side, told me to write to him and explain that I had lied about Julio; tell him I still loved him and wanted him more than anything in the world. The other half of me, the sensible, protective half, advised caution. After all, just because he had jilted Maruja didn't necessarily imply that he still loved me – or that he ever had. He might, as Anita believed, be just another playboy, amusing himself with different girls and tiring of them all the time. For all I knew, he might already have another girlfriend in Madrid. Anyway, I had learned to live without him so why burn my fingers in the fire again?

When Easter came I knew he must have been back in Burgos, but I neither saw him nor received any communication from him. I decided my cautious side had been right so I would follow its directive and leave things as they were.

Sundays were usually spent with our group of friends in the bars or at the cinema. Sergio continued his hopeless pursuit of Marisol and it amazed me that it was taking him so long to realize he hadn't a chance of winning her affections. Felipe was becoming excited at the prospect of a new bullfighting season ahead and bored us all with details of Luis Miguel Dominguín's latest feats in the rings of Madrid and Seville.

Anita hardly ever joined us as her Sundays were mostly taken up with Desmond who still came regularly to see her. However, of late I had detected something I hardly dared to imagine: a slight waning in her devotion to him. I noticed that she now read his letters with less eagerness and even, occasionally, stifled a yawn or two. Also, by this time, she had found herself a new job at the Provincial Hospital and one of the young newly-qualified doctors there had been paying her considerable attention. I awaited further developments with bated breath.

May was a sad month for the family as we were to lose Teo's company. The time had come for the army to claim the next two years of his life, interrupting his studies and disrupting his plans. He was studying Law in the optimistic hope that this might, some day, provide him with a worthwhile career. However, he was sufficiently realistic to know that this was unlikely, as finding a good job in Spain depended on who you knew and your political background rather than suitable qualifications. Most institutions were riddled with corruption, something to which the people were now resigned.

The day we saw him off at the station was warm. The wind had, at last, dropped and the sun was making its strength felt. Teo looked uncomfortable and forlorn in his uniform as he stood waiting on the platform, his kit bag beside him, for the train that would take him and his fellow recruits to Madrid on the first stage of their journey to Morocco. When the train arrived, twenty minutes late, Anita clung to him tearfully, loath to let him go, tugging at his jacket as he climbed up to join the other sweating men in the corridor. He fought his way to a window and leaned out. Anita rushed over, grasping his hand and gazing up at him with a tear-stained face as she begged him to write soon. Teo reassured her. He would be okay, of course he would write and no, he hadn't forgotten his packed lunch and was looking forward to the *chorizo* sandwiches.

The train pulled out and we ran alongside it, waving frantically until it gained speed and carried him away into the distance. We walked disconsolately back to the house, missing him already and when Anita noticed his guitar hanging lonely on the wall, she broke down completely. Teo was more than a brother to Anita. He was her best friend and they had never been apart before.

"Why should he have to become a soldier?" she cried out angrily when her tears were spent. "Why should he have to take orders from *them*? He hates them! They killed our father! They're ruining our country!"

I tried to calm her down but it was several days before she showed signs of recovery and certainly the absence of his jovial presence and lively singing was felt by all of us. That year, also, Anita had begun her *servicio social*, a compulsory training programme for girls which she had to attend regularly and bitterly resented. She would drag herself off to those dreary evening sessions with extreme reluctance and return from them looking thoroughly fed up. One day I asked her what they did.

"Oh, we learn to be good mothers, good Spanish wives and

mothers and then we have political instruction. Well, you can imagine what that is! Oh, and then we have to pray too. But what I pray for in my heart is that we could be a free country again!"

"It sounds very boring. I'm glad we've nothing like that at home."

"You don't know how lucky you are," she remarked, getting up from the table where we had been playing cards and going over to the stove to make coffee.

"The worst thing about this evening," she added, pouring it into cups, "is that I could have been out with Víctor."

"Víctor?"

"Yes," she gave one of her dreamy sighs. "He asked me out tonight."

"You mean that young doctor, don't you? The one with the glasses and the big smile?"

She sighed again. "Yes. He's just qualified and he's going to be a marvellous doctor. This is his first job and do you know what they want him to do?"

I shook my head, secretly delighted at her interest in this new admirer.

"They're sending him to the bullring every Sunday to see to bullfighters who might get hurt."

"I bet Felipe will be jealous! Wouldn't he just love the chance to see all the bullfights in Burgos for free?"

"But Víctor isn't like Felipe. He's not like anyone else I've ever known."

"I seem to have heard that story before. Surely you can't be in love *again*? How about Desmond? I thought he was the great love of your life. I thought you were supposed to be *novios*?"

Anita put her head on one side, considering her reply. "Well," she began thoughtfully, "I suppose we are. I know he loves me and he's very romantic and I'm really fond of him – you know that – but one can't always be completely sure, can one? I mean you're not completely sure about Julio, are you?"

"I never have been," I reminded her. "We're just good friends and that's all. It's nothing serious: not like you and Desmond."

"Oh, we're not that serious really," she said lightly. "It was fun while it lasted but I don't think it can go on for ever."

I felt immensely relieved on hearing this and was overcome with gratitude to this smiling, myopic doctor who seemed on course to rescue Anita from a lifetime of Desmond Brocklebank.

છ ૪૦

It was about this time that I started to feel seriously homesick. Letters from my family reminded me that it was spring in England, something I was sorely missing. Lying stiff and cramped in my bed, I would imagine myself back in the Somerset home of my childhood, warm and cosy in my familiar little bedroom, waking to the call of the cuckoo, listening to the sparrows chattering in the thatch above my window. I imagined myself pulling back the curtains, looking down at the long shadows spreading across the daisy-sprinkled lawn, the ornamental cherry smothered in pink blossoms and the drifts of daffodils nestling among lush grass. In my imagination I could smell the fresh, damp fragrance of an English spring morning and hear the lambs bleating in distant meadows. I dreamt of woodlands carpeted with primroses and then I realised it was May already and there would be bluebells in the woods, cowslips in the meadows and cow parsley lining the country lanes. Never, in these idyllic fantasies, was there room for the reality of my working life, for the depressing world of London bed-sits, the dreary jungle of buildings, the dust and grime, the smell of exhaust, the hustle and bustle of city life to which I would shortly be returning.

These reflections made me aware, also, of just how much I was missing my family; hearing my mother playing the piano, my father listening to the cricket commentary, and bike rides with my sister. I also missed a lot of practical things such as a hot bath, comfortable chairs, a *real* cup of tea! I missed the luxury of speaking my own language and I was even looking forward to the company of Englishmen again. After the traumas of the past few months, it would make a refreshing change to be among sensible, steady, reliable Englishmen: not passionate, not jealous, not obsessed with pride, honour and machismo. Men who didn't notice the colour of your eyes or your hair, who treated you like one of the lads, explained to you the finer features of their car engines.

All this nostalgia for home made me stop at the bank one morning on the way to my classes, to ask for a statement of my account. I was relieved to discover that I had already saved enough for my return journey. I was free to go home any time I wished and end this strange life to which I had now become so accustomed. I walked out of the bank into the sunshine, wondering what I should do. I could stay until the beginning of August and then I would have to go whatever happened, as my work permit lasted only one year. Every three months I had to report to the police. They liked to keep tabs on everybody, not only aliens, but their own people too. When Anita and I had stayed in *pensiones*, we had to surrender our documents: Anita her identity card and I, my passport. They were kept for several hours, usually overnight, so that our whereabouts could be reported to the authorities.

Fortunately, I was on fairly good terms with the police in Burgos, deeming it wise to keep on the right side of them. They knew me and would chat and joke when I visited their headquarters with my passport. "You must like it here," they would say, "since you want to stay another three months. That's good! That's good!"

Now I had to decide whether or not to apply for those last three months till August and I was very torn. I thought back on all the strange events that had happened to me since that hot summer's afternoon when I stepped off the train at Burgos and first set eyes on Anita, standing there so trim and pretty next to Vázquez. Since that day I had enjoyed such adventures, seen so many places and met so many interesting people and I had become familiar with every nook and cranny of this friendly, crumbling place; so could I say goodbye to it already?

From the bank, I made my way through the narrow back streets towards the *Capitanía*. Under the hot sun, everything was flooded in a dazzling brilliance and the atmosphere was clear and dry, quite unlike the oppressive, damp heat of an English summer.

The harsh, blinding light made the shadows deep and dark. As I emerged into the main square, a group of women were gathered round the communal fountain with their jugs, their animated chatter mingling with the splash of water. I remembered that when I first arrived in Burgos, I was amazed to see that even in a city of this size, so many households were without mains water. Water, something which we took for granted back home, was a precious commodity here and I had learned to respect it. So many things which had seemed strange to me at first, I now accepted as normal. I was beginning to feel like a Spaniard. I was even thinking and dreaming in Spanish!

I no longer feared the house of the Captain General. Those guards who, on the first day had seemed so terrifying, I now knew to be ordinary young men. Some of them I had seen and recognised off duty and they had even paid me the odd compliment! I knew most of the domestic staff by their first names and was confident of a warm welcome when I was shown into the room where the daughters had their lessons. That particular day was no exception.

"How glad we are to see you! We have finished that long translation you gave us but we are not sure of one point of grammar. Magdalena and I have been arguing about it all weekend. Come and settle the matter for us!"

I crossed the room cautiously, keeping a wary eye on one of the cats that was crouching menacingly, behind a chair. Experience had taught me that some of the younger ones were in the habit of springing out on unsuspecting passers-by and clawing at their legs. Because of this, I had had several pairs of nylons ruined and suffered some painful scratches.

"Come and sit down," said Magdalena. "You look very hot. Would you like some lemonade?"

"Here are our translations," said Elisa eagerly, gathering up a pile of papers and setting them before me, "I think you will find that I have written that first sentence correctly but Magdalena says I was wrong."

Their enthusiasm made them easy to teach. To them it was an absorbing hobby, something which had helped them to while away the long Burgos winter, a challenge, a game, an excuse for friendly rivalry. I knew they would miss the lessons enormously when I left.

Having corrected their work, I said: "Señoritas, I have to make an important decision. My parents want me home as soon as possible and I don't know what to do: whether to go now or wait till August."

"Wait!" they cried in chorus.

"Don't leave us now!" pleaded Elisa. "Not yet. Please! Would your parents mind so *very* much if you waited till August? Would you like us to write to them and ask them if you can stay a little longer?"

I laughed. "It's entirely up to me. I have a very understanding family and they don't interfere in my life."

My pupils looked a little puzzled. In a society where parents still seemed to have complete control over their grown-up offspring, particularly their daughters, this didn't make sense.

"Anyway," I said cheerfully, "I can recommend a very good teacher to take my place. Don Federico Suárez. You'll like him."

Magdalena shook her head sadly. "It won't be the same." she said.

"In the meantime, back to the lesson. I shall read the story on page thirty-one and then you will read it to me in turn."

As I read the lesson to them slowly, carefully enunciating each word, I was aware of sounds outside in the passage, followed by the door at the end of the room behind me being opened and closed quietly. One of the cats that had been sitting high up on a shelf basking in a patch of sunlight, looked up sharply, staring beyond me into the room. Then it rose to its feet, stretching its legs and arching its back before jumping lightly to the floor and padding past me, tail erect. Someone had entered the room and was now standing close behind me, casting a shadow onto the book. I stopped reading and looked up.

"Hello Papá," said Elisa. "This is the English señorita – our teacher."

The Captain General was smaller than I had expected. I had imagined him tall, stiff and tight-lipped with cold, cruel eyes, rather like a head of the German Gestapo as portrayed in films about the Second World War: the kind who stands behind a desk, fixing his cowering victims with a steely stare and informing them they have "vays of making you talk". I was surprised, therefore, to see a short, stout, grey-haired man with a cat curled round his shoulders. Certainly he was resplendent in an impressive uniform and there was something slightly sinister about his shiny high boots, but he was smiling at me in a friendly manner and it was hard to believe he could inspire such fear. We shook hands and he asked me about his daughters' progress. "Are you satisfied with them? Are they good students?" I assured him that they were. "Good, good!" he said. "Please, continue your lesson. Do not let me interrupt you." He remained there for a few minutes, watching us and stroking the cat, then he slipped away as quietly as he had come and I never saw him again.

Sipping ice-cold lemonade at the end of the lesson, the girls asked me if I had come to a decision about returning to England. Two pairs of dark eyes, their lashes sticky with mascara, were looking at me expectantly. I shook my head. "Not yet. I'm still thinking about it."

Outside the *Capitania*, I stood thoughtfully for a few minutes, watching the mule carts trundling by and listening to the sing-song voices of the lottery ticket sellers. Then, having checked that I had my passport with me, I set off in the direction of the Police Station.

 CB   BD

The days grew longer and warmer and soon we were again sweltering under that pitiless sun I had come to know the previous summer. As the weeks went by, Anita's interest in Desmond continued to decline at the same time as her passion for Víctor increased. This time, she assured me, she was quite sure of her feelings. This was the real thing and there could never be anyone else in her life. He had proposed to her and she had accepted so that made them *novios formales*, an engaged couple, planning to spend the rest of their lives together. The only snag was Desmond.

Of course, she had tried to soften the blow by hinting in her letters that she was beginning to have doubts, paving the way for the moment when he would have to learn the truth. Naturally, this caused him to become highly suspicious and things came to a head one hot Sunday morning when Desmond, having travelled up from Madrid unexpectedly, came upon Anita and Víctor walking arm in arm along the Espolón.

I was not present on this memorable occasion, but according to eye witness accounts, a terrible scene ensued. So incensed was Desmond that the Spanish side of him took full possession of his behaviour and he showered the pair of them with a torrent of angry abuse. She, Anita, the girl of his dreams, was a false goddess! She, his faultless Aphrodite, had at last revealed herself in her true colours. She was nothing but a shameless Jezebel, a treacherous siren who lured men to destruction. As for Víctor, he was a villain, a swine, a snake in the grass, a callous Casanova who stole the hearts of other men's women. He would pay for his actions. Honour, the honour of Desmond Brocklebank, must be satisfied. He had then made various threatening gestures towards Víctor who removed his thick spectacles, cleaned them hastily on his hanky and replaced them to assess his rival with clearer vision. Despite his studious and amiable appearance, Víctor's spirit was as proud and jealous as any self-respecting Spanish male and he was swift to prepare himself for verbal and, if necessary, physical battle. They argued and insulted each other and would indeed have come to blows but for the intervention of Anita and various friends who happened to be passing and came running to her assistance. The angry men were forcibly separated and Anita told Desmond very firmly, that their relationship was at an end.

"It's incredible," I said to Don Federico as I recounted these events to him the morning after they happened. "It's really amazing how worked up you Spanish get over things like women and honour. In England, if a love affair or something goes wrong, we might become very depressed, but we don't fly into these awful passions."

Federico raised his eyebrows, his eyes narrowing. "Ah" he said, poking his cigarette in my direction, "I know how you call that. Is *stiff upper lip!* No?"

"I suppose you could call it that."

Federico closed his eyes and nodded with satisfaction. "Yes, you see I know these things. You British have stiff upper lip but that does not mean you do not feel the same like as we do. You too feel jealousy and jealousy turns to hate. Your own poet says: *yield up, O Love, thy crown and hearted throne to tyrannous hate!* Othello, Act three, Scene three. Your poet speaks much of jealousy."

"Yes, of course we feel jealous at times but we don't make such a song and dance of it."

"Othello did."

"But Othello was a *Moor*! Perhaps it's the Moorish blood that makes Spaniards so jealous."

Federico drained his glass. "You want another drink?" he enquired, pointing to my empty one.

"Another beer, please Federico. This heat is terrible. It makes me so thirsty."

"We have one more here and then we go to Paco's place. I have to speak with La Morena."

"I... I'm afraid I can't come with you. I have to go to the travel agency to book my tickets home."

"So soon you are going? It is only July."

"My ex-boss," I explained, "the one I worked for in London, has offered me a job again. It's a better job with more money. Now that my Spanish is fluent and I can type properly, he wants me to be his new secretary. But I have to go home at once or I shall lose this opportunity. Oh Freddie! I shall miss you so much! You and all my friends – and Burgos. It makes me want to cry when I think about it."

"But you will come back? You will come back soon?"

"Of course."

"I too will miss you. Who will roll for me my cigarettes?"

We laughed and he spread his tobacco and papers on the bar for me. I started to roll him rather lumpy little cigarettes for, despite his patient tuition, I had not yet properly mastered this art. The bar tender laughed when he brought our drinks. "*Vaya!* Federico, you got her well trained!" he remarked.

Federico stood watching my efforts in thoughtful silence for some minutes. Then, all of a sudden, he said: "Is funny. You talk to me of Spanish pride and honour but you people also are proud. *You* are a very proud girl. You know that?"

"Me? Why do you say that?" I looked up from my task in surprise.

"Because is true. You suffer a lot but you say nothing. Stiff upper lip! You want something very much but you say no because you are too proud."

"Federico, I haven't the faintest idea what you're talking about."

"I think you have. I have seen your lover the other day. I have seen Luis. He is in Burgos now and he wants to see you. I think you still feel something for him, no?"

"NO!" I told him emphatically, feeling the blood rush to my cheeks.

Federico picked up one of my cigarettes and tapped it on the counter before placing it in his mouth. "But you are lying, aren't you?" he suggested gently.

"Yes," I confessed miserably. "Yes! Yes! Yes! I am. But there's nothing I can do about it now. It's too late. I'm going back to England next week."

Federico lit the cigarette. "I say no more," he said, shaking out his match. "Now you tell me the truth I shut up about it. We bury Caesar like you say."

☙ ❧

The following Sunday afternoon I found myself sitting with Anita in the shade of some scrubby bushes half way up the hill behind the town. We had decided to climb the *castillo*, where it was quiet and we could enjoy a long, uninterrupted conversation. It would be our last chance of doing so for a long time. That afternoon there was an important bullfight taking place in the dilapidated Plaza de Toros. Víctor, much to his annoyance, was on duty there, ready for any casualties. He resented having to spend two or three hours of his precious Sunday afternoon in this way when he could have been with Anita.

The grass felt dry and prickly beneath my legs and I was uneasily aware of the fact that there were giant ants crawling around in the vicinity. They were three times the size of English ants and their stings twice as painful. I did not trust them and, from time to time, I felt obliged to get up and inspect the place where I had been sitting. The air was heavy with the scent of wild thyme and cypress and all around grew curious plants that I had never seen before. They had to be extremely hardy, I thought, to withstand both the rigours of those long cruel winters and the scorching heat of summer. It had not rained for weeks and the ground was rock hard, dusty and cracked, yet still they flourished and flowered. I felt sure they would share with me the distinction of being among Desmond's "Hardy Weeds".

Below us, the tall towers and spires of the cathedral, the rusty-pink roofs of the houses and the squat belfries of distant churches and monasteries all lay shimmering in the relentless heat, under a dark blue sky. Faintly, from one of the houses at the foot of the hill, the strains of a radio playing Spanish music could be heard. I gazed wistfully at the familiar scene: the great, arid *meseta* stretching out behind the town, greyish-yellow and treeless like an endless desert, disappearing into the horizon. All this would soon be nothing but a memory.

"First Teo has to go away and now you," complained Anita, plucking a piece of grass and nibbling at it. "The house will be so quiet tomorrow. Just Auntie Domi and me."

"Never mind, you've got Víctor. He's here all the time and you're lucky to have such a great boyfriend."

"I know. I'm very happy with Víctor but that won't stop me missing you. You're the best friend I've ever had and we've had such adventures together. All that fun in Andalusia! It couldn't have happened if we hadn't met."

"And I've been really happy here. I feel like one of the family now and I'm going to miss you all such a lot."

"We're like sisters. I hope it will always be like this, whatever happens in the future. Oh! Do you *have* to go so soon?"

"I have my own family," I reminded her. "And I haven't seen my parents for nearly a year."

"Yes, of course," Anita sighed. "You have your own parents. You're lucky to have them. I wish I had mine."

I felt like kicking myself. Why did I have to be so tactless? I would divert our conversation to another subject.

"Anita, I have a problem and since you're my sister here in Spain, you must advise me. Luis is back in Burgos and Federico says he wants to see me. He hasn't a *novia* any more and I would like to see him again if only to say goodbye. It would be easy. All I have to do is go round to Paco's..."

Anita, who had been lying down, sat up abruptly. "Are you mad? Of course you mustn't see him. Can't you see he's just playing around with your feelings? If he'd been serious about you he would have written to you ages ago. Look what he's done to the Institute gardener's daughter! Thrown her aside as though she were an old coat! Callously discarded her after all the time they'd been together. The poor girl's heart-broken! You can't be serious. He's nothing but a playboy."

I said nothing but my face betrayed my emotions.

"I thought you'd finished with him, forgotten him. Look! I pleased you by ending my romance with Desmond and finding someone else. I know you never approved of Desmond and me, now will you please do the same for me? Just forget Luis. He's no good for you. I know it, so just forget him. Go back and find yourself a nice Englishman!"

At that point this rather uncomfortable conversation was interrupted by someone calling to us from below and we saw Marisol climbing up towards us and waving. A few feet behind her trudged another figure who, as they drew nearer, proved unsurprisingly, to be Sergio.

"Hello you two! So *there* you are. I called at the house and Domi said you were up here." She turned to me. "I've got something for you."

Marisol was looking pretty in a sleeveless summer dress. She was holding a small packet wrapped in fancy gift paper. "Catch!" she said, tossing it into my lap. "It's nothing much, just a small present for you to take back to England. Some cologne, that's all, so don't get too excited!"

Over the last few days I had been overwhelmed with presents from all my pupils and friends: bottles of wine and brandy, sweets, perfume, decorative plates, models of fighting bulls, fans. I was beginning to wonder how I could possibly transport this mountain of gifts to England.

A few minutes later, we were joined by Sergio looking hot and panting slightly from his recent exertion. He flopped down on the grass beside us and dabbed his forehead with a hanky. "Mother of God! What heat!" he exclaimed.

"Why, Sergio!" Marisol feigned surprise. "I didn't realise you'd followed me all the way up here. Did you want to see me about something?"

"Not really. Just thought I'd come and keep you company and say goodbye to our *inglesa*."

"I've had an idea," I said. "Let's all go down and have a drink in the town. We'll find Gonzalo and the others and pick up Víctor and Felipe from the bullring. Then we'll all have a farewell drink on me."

"Done!" said Anita, getting to her feet and brushing the grass and dust from her dress. "Just as long as it isn't at the Bar La Morena," she added, giving me a significant nudge.

ᑕᓏ ᐧᓎ

As I hurried along the Calle de Santander the following morning, I was vaguely aware of two tall young men passing me from the opposite direction. I didn't notice who they were as my mind was busy making lists of things still to be sorted out and packed before catching my train to France that afternoon. I had been to the travel agency to collect my tickets and was wondering whether I had made a mistake in not paying the extra for a couchette from Irún to Paris, when I heard an excited voice calling my name. I turned round and saw Paco, sun-tanned and smiling, his vivacious dark eyes seeking me out, as jaunty and good-humoured as ever. I knew who was with him but hardly dared to look, feeling madly excited and terrified at the same time.

"What luck! We've caught you! Federico said you were off to England soon," said Paco.

"This afternoon." My voice was a hoarse whisper.

Paco caught me firmly by the arm. "Then you *must* come and have a drink with us. No excuses this time."

We started walking towards the Espolón and Luis changed places with Paco and was now walking beside me.

"I didn't realise you were going so soon," he said. "I've been wanting so much to see you."

The sound of his soft voice caused me to tremble and I forced myself to look at him. I was amazed to see how healthy he was looking. His face was fuller, there was colour in his cheeks and his green eyes were clear and bright beneath the thick, black lashes. Everything I had ever felt for him came flooding back with a vengeance. I could hardly believe I was not dreaming, that I wouldn't wake up to harsh reality any minute. But this time it was not a fantasy. The phantom Luis had materialised into real flesh and blood. He could be touched without melting into thin air!

"You... you look so well, Luis," I stammered wishing my heart would stop its violent pounding. "You look so much better than the last time I saw you."

He smiled at me. "You too look well. You look wonderful, as lovely as ever."

Flatterer! I thought, mindful of Anita's words, maybe he *is* just like the rest of them with empty compliments designed to ensnare females.

Paco said suddenly: "Look you two! I can't stop. I've just remembered I've got to get back to help behind the bar. My mother will be busy with lunches. Forgive me if I leave you but have a good trip and don't forget us!"

With these words he hugged me briefly and then disappeared among the throng of people taking their pre-lunch stroll along the Espolón.

"He's a good friend," said Luis.

"I'm afraid I can't be long either," I said truthfully. "I've got to get back to finish my packing. I'm catching a train at five."

"But you have a little time, surely? Come on! Let's go for a walk along by the river. There's so much we have to talk about."

We walked for a few minutes in silence, awkwardly, like the

first time we had been alone together. We reached the Isla and stopped under the shade of some trees, the same place where we had often lingered in the past. He leaned on the parapet, gazing down into the water which was now flowing at a sluggish pace, fast evaporating in the searing heat.

"How is Maruja?" I enquired in mock ignorance, but wishing to hear the truth from the horse's mouth.

"I don't know. I haven't seen her for ages. You must know we've broken up. After knowing you, I couldn't go on with Maruja. It would have been dishonest because I no longer felt anything for her."

"You're a Don Juan, just like the rest."

Luis looked genuinely surprised. He laughed. "I've been called many things − but never that! They all tell me I'm too shy with girls."

"So what have you been doing in Madrid, apart from your studies? Have you found a new girlfriend?"

He shook his head. "There's a group of us at university, all socialist students − that is nearly all of us although there are some communists and anarchists as well, and we meet in secret. Next term we're planning a demonstration. We've a lot of support, we'll bring the whole campus out on the streets. That should shake them!"

"*Oh no*, Luis! I don't believe this! Will you never learn? You mustn't become a political agitator! They'll kill you."

He laughed. "Yes, they might try. They'll probably bring out their machine guns to subdue us but it's worth the risk. I don't care."

"Don't do it!" I pleaded. "Please don't! I don't want anything to happen to you. Listen to me!"

He turned to look at me. "I love you," he said softly.

My head was spinning from a combination of intense heat and emotional turmoil and I had to cling to the parapet to steady myself. "If that's true," I responded faintly, "then you will listen to me and you won't have anything to do with political demonstrations."

"My feelings for you are just the same," he continued, ignoring my entreaties, "and if it weren't for Julio…"

"Julio isn't my *novio*.. We're just friends."

"But you said…"

"Yes, I know what I said but it was a lie because I felt so hurt about Maruja."

I stared at him, wide-eyed, gripping the parapet and wondering what effect this confession would have, but he just laughed and shook his head, eyes fixed on the ground. "If you were trying to get your own back you certainly succeeded – and I deserved it," he said.

"We've made ourselves pretty miserable, haven't we? Anyway, what's the use? It's all over now and I've got to go home. In a few hours I shall be on the train and goodness knows when I'll be back in Spain."

Luis caught my hand. "Federico hinted to me that there was hope, that you still loved me, and as I told you before, it can never be over between us. Can I write to you? Will you let me do that?"

I nodded, trying to stay calm. So now I knew what Don Federico was up to with his persistent questioning of my emotions. The trouble was he read too much Shakespeare and obviously fancied himself in that Friar Lawrence rôle! Luis felt around in his pocket and produced an empty cigarette packet and a biro. "Your address," he said, handing them to me. I wrote it out in block capitals, using the top of the parapet as a table.

"That's my home address," I explained, "and it will always find me, although I may not be there long as I'll be working in London."

I watched him study it carefully, his green eyes narrowing slightly as he sought to decipher the unfamiliar words.

"Oh, and by the way," I added, unable to suppress my feelings any longer, "Federico was right."

He pushed the packet with my address into his pocket, smiled broadly, and stretching out his arms, grasped me tightly to him. I felt his warm lips on my neck and mouth, his hands gently caressing me and for some time we stayed locked in that embrace, in an ecstasy of happiness. But such public displays of affection were frowned on in Franco's Spain and could attract the attention of the police so, reluctantly, we at last drew apart and had to content ourselves with gazing longingly at each other over glasses of white wine before walking, arms entwined, back to Anita's house.

So that was how it happened. I had given Luis my address and by doing so, had opened a door through which he could re-enter my life. I knew that ignoring Anita's warnings could be a mistake, but teenage love is reckless and how could I know what the future might hold?

These thoughts were passing through my mind as the Irún express pulled out of the station that afternoon and I waved my last goodbyes to Anita, Domi and my life in Spain. Leaning out of the window and watching the spires of Burgos cathedral recede into the distance as the train gathered speed, I suddenly recalled some lines of verse I had once come across by an American poet, Sara Teasdale. They went like this:

When I can look life in the eyes,
Grown calm and very coldly wise,
Life will have given me the truth,
And taken in exchange – my youth.